Studies in Modern Chemistry

Advanced courses in chemistry are changing
rapidly in both structure and content. The changes
have led to a demand for up-to-date books that
present recent developments clearly and concisely.
This series is meant to provide advanced students
with books that will bridge the gap between the
standard textbook and research paper. The
books should also be useful to a chemist who
requires a survey of current work outside his own
field of research. Mathematical treatment has been
kept as simple as is consistent with clear
understanding of the subject.
Careful selection of authors actively engaged in
research in each field, together with the guidance of
four experienced editors, has ensured that
each book ideally suits the needs of persons
seeking a comprehensible and modern treatment
of rapidly developing areas of chemistry.

William C. Agosta, The Rockefeller University
R. S. Nyholm, FRS, University College London

Consulting Editors

Studies in Modern Chemistry

Non-aqueous solvents

T. C. Waddington

University of Warwick

APPLETON-CENTURY-CROFTS

EDUCATIONAL DIVISION

New York MEREDITH CORPORATION

Appleton-Century-Crofts
Educational Division
Meredith Corporation
440 Park Avenue South
New York, N.Y. 10016

Printed in Great Britain

Contents

Preface

This book is based on courses of lectures given to final year undergraduates in chemistry at the Universities of Cambridge and Warwick. A basic knowledge of the physical chemistry of ionic solutions and of basic electrochemistry is assumed. Its intention is not to be comprehensive in the range of topics covered but to give students a comparative view of the chemistry of non-aqueous solvents, both protonic and non-protonic. Obviously, many important solvent systems are not even mentioned, but I hope that a fairly complete coverage of the principles that govern non-aqueous solvent behaviour is given.

T. C. Waddington

Solute–solvent interaction

1-1 Energetics of solvation

The chemistry of ionizing solvents is essentially the study of the properties of those solvents and their solutions in which the interaction with solutes, be they covalent compounds or ionic crystals, is sufficiently strong to produce ions in solution. In view of the strength of the forces holding ionic crystals together and the size of the energies required to produce heterolytic fission of covalent bonds the energies of these solvent–solute interactions must be very considerable, probably between 50 and 100 kcal mol^{-1} per g-ion produced.

It must be admitted at this stage that there is no adequate quantitative theory which will predict the nature and size of these forces for a wide range of solvents and that even a completely adequate qualitative theory is lacking, although a number of useful empirical guide-lines to behaviour will be discussed later in this chapter. However, once the ions are produced in solution, then at moderate dilution it is possible to rationalize their behaviour and conductivity by theories in which the only solvent parameter is the dielectric constant.

The earliest quantitative treatment of the solvent–ionic solute interaction attempted to rationalize the energy of interaction of an ion with its solvent in terms of the behaviour of a dielectric in the field of a charged sphere. Simple electrostatic arguments show that if a sphere of radius R, carrying a charge q, is moved from vacuum to a solvent of dielectric constant ϵ, there is a free energy change:

$$\Delta G = \frac{q^2}{2R} \left(1 - \frac{1}{\epsilon} \right)$$

or, per g-ion:

$$\Delta G = -\frac{N_A z^2 e^2}{2R} \left(1 - \frac{1}{\epsilon} \right)$$

where ze is the charge on the ion, e being the electronic charge and z the valency, and N_A is Avogadro's constant. The corresponding enthalpy change is:

$$\Delta H = -\frac{N_A z^2 e^2}{2R}\left(1 - \frac{1}{\epsilon} - \frac{T}{\epsilon^2}\cdot\frac{\partial\epsilon}{\partial T}\right)$$

Such a theory is clearly a gross approximation, for the solvent near the ion cannot be treated as a continuous dielectric and in the ion's immediate neighbourhood the electric fields are so intense that the solvent molecules are likely to be coordinated. In addition there is the problem of what value one takes for the radius of the ion in solution. However, the formulae do offer an estimate of the energies involved and in Table 1-1 values are given of the energies of solvation on this model for different values of R (in Å) and ϵ.

Table 1-1   **Effect of dielectric constant on free energy of solvation**

The 'Born charging equation' is used, R is the radius of the ion in Å, ϵ the dielectric constant of the solvent. Free energies are given in kcal mol^{-1}.

R \ ϵ	2	4	8	16	32	64	128	∞
0·5	166	249	291	311	322	326	329	332
1·0	83	124	145	156	161	163	165	166
1·5	55	83	97	104	107	109	110	111
2·0	42	62	73	78	80	82	82	83
3·0	28	42	48	52	54	54	55	55
4·0	21	31	36	39	40	41	41	41
5·0	17	25	29	31	32	32	33	33
10·0	8	12	15	16	16	16	17	17

Some general points emerge from this table. Clearly for really small ions like Li$^+$ (crystal radius = 0·68 Å) and Na$^+$ (crystal radius = 0·98 Å) the solvation energies are very large and it is not surprising to find that salts containing these cations, particularly when the anions are large and the lattice energies consequently low, are soluble in solvents of quite low dielectric constant. Second, the change in the solvation energy on increase of dielectric constant above a value of ϵ of about 30 is relatively small, and so one would expect all materials with dielectric constants above about 30 to be quite good ionizing solvents. Table 1-2 lists the dielectric constants of some ionizing solvents.

Since liquids with a dielectric constant of over 30 are inevitably associated to some degree, other physical properties tend to be related to good solvent behaviour. Association usually means that the freezing and boiling points are higher than one would expect from a simple consideration of the molecular weight, e.g. compare the boiling

Table 1-2   **Dielectric constants of a number of ionizing solvents at 25°C (unless otherwise stated)**

Solvent	ϵ	Solvent	ϵ
H_2SO_4	100	I_2	11·1 (118°C)
$CH_3 \cdot CO \cdot N(CH_3)_2$	37·8	Br_2	3·12 (20°C)
$CH_3 \cdot CO \cdot NH(CH_3)$	165·5 (40°C)	$AsCl_3$	12·6 (17°C)
$(CH_3)_2SO$	46·6	$SbCl_3$	33·0 (75°C)
$CH_3 \cdot NO_2$	35.9	SO_2	15·4 (0°C)
$C_6H_5 \cdot NO_2$	34·8	NH_3	23 (-33°C)
$(CH_3)_2CO$	20·7		16·90
$CH_3 \cdot OH$	32·6	HF	175 (-73°C)
$C_2H_5 \cdot OH$	24·3		84 (0°C)
C_5H_5N	12·3	HCl	9·28 (-95°C)
$CH_3 \cdot CN$	36·2	HBr	7·0 (-85°C)
NOCl	22·5 ($-27·5$°C)	H_2O	78·30
$POCl_3$	13·9 (20°C)		

points of water, ammonia, and hydrogen fluoride with those of hydrogen sulphide, phosphine, and hydrogen chloride. One would also expect that, as associated liquids, good solvents would exhibit anomalous Trouton's constants with higher values than that of 21·5 found for unassociated liquids.

1-2   The nature of solvent–solute interactions

Modifications of the continuum theory of ion solvation outlined above have usually considered that the solvent molecules in the first layer around the ion in solution have their dipoles oriented by the ionic charge and are coordinated either by ion–dipole forces or by co-ordinate bonds. Interactions outside the first coordination sphere are then treated by a continuum model. This type of treatment has produced, in the case of water, good agreement between the sums of theoretically calculated solvation energies for pairs of positive and negative univalent ions and the experimental values. Clearly a high solvent dipole moment will favour a high interaction energy with a solute ion. Some solvent dipole moments are given in Table 1-3.

Ion–dipole interactions are obviously the main source of the solvation energy of the alkali metal ions, but when transition metal ions are considered actual donation of an electron pair *from* solvent molecules to the ion takes place and, clearly, physical measurements that assess the power of coordination will give a measure of solvent power. With negative ions, electrostatic ion–dipole forces are for many solvents the only type of interaction that can take place. There are, however, two fairly specific types of interaction that can occur in some systems between the solvent and negative ions.

Table 1-3 Dipole moments of a number of ionizing solvents

Solvent	Dipole moment (Debye units)	Solvent	Dipole moment (Debye units)
H_2O	1·85	$CH_3 \cdot OH$	1·70
HF	1·82	$C_2H_5 \cdot OH$	1·69
NH_3	1·47	$AsCl_3$	1·59
HCl	1·08	$SOCl_2$	1·45
$(CH_3)_2SO$	3·96	NOCl	1·83
C_5H_5N	2·1	NO_2	0·316
$CH_3 \cdot CN$	3·92	$(CH_3)_2CO$	2·88
SO_2	1·63	$CH_3 \cdot NO_2$	3·46
$CH_3 \cdot CO \cdot N(CH_3)_2$	3·81	$C_6H_5 \cdot NO_2$	4·22
$CH_3 \cdot CO \cdot NH(CH_3)$	3·73		

Hydrogen bonds may form when the solvent possesses polar hydrogen atoms. Another type of interaction that may occur is donation of electron pairs from the negative ion *to* the solvent.

The strongest and most effective solvents are those which, in addition to having a high dielectric constant and a largish molecular dipole moment, can interact with both positive and negative ions in one of the specific ways mentioned above. Thus, water forms strong coordinate bonds with transition metal ions and can also hydrogen bond strongly with negative ions such as fluoride, chloride, bromide, hydroxide, etc.

In some cases, usually when transition metal ions and halide ions are involved, there is an actual competition between the halide ions and the solvent in coordination with the metal ion. Consider, for example, cobaltous chloride, $CoCl_2$. In dilute aqueous solutions, the ions present are $Co(OH_2)_6^{2+}$ and Cl^-, and the solution has a characteristically pale pink colour. In solvents of lower dielectric constant and of lower coordination power—such as acetone—a whole range of species $CoCl_4^{2-}$, $CoCl_3S^-$, $CoCl_2S_4$, $CoClS_5^+$, and CoS_6^{2+} occur. Such solutions are characterized by a deep blue colour due to the tetrahedral species $CoCl_4^{2-}$ and $CoCl_3S^-$ (S represents a solvent molecule).

1-3 Measurements of 'solvent strength'

A wide variety of physical techniques has been suggested for use as a measure of solvent donor strengths, though relatively few as a measure of solvent acceptor strengths, and some measurements have been used as a measure of 'solvent strength' in general.

In the vast majority of solvents an ion such as Ni^{2+} is octahedrally coordinated by solvent molecules. Ligand field theory tells us that in such a situation the energy levels of the d-electron orbitals on the

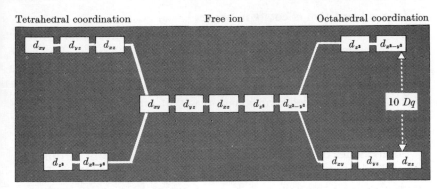

Fig. 1-1 Ligand-field splitting in octahedral and tetrahedral coordination.

nickel ion will be split into two groups, the e_g and the t_{2g} levels (Fig. 1-1).

Transitions between these levels are possible and they give rise to the characteristic ligand-field absorptions in the electronic spectrum of the coordinated ion. Such transitions occur in the visible and near-infrared regions of the electromagnetic spectrum. Measurement of their wavelengths enables us to calculate the energy difference between the e_g and the t_{2g} levels. This difference is usually denoted by $10Dq$ and the value of Dq in cm^{-1} gives a measure of the solvent donor strength. Typical values are given in Table 1-4. It will be seen that the ligand field splittings do not correlate with the dielectric constants and dipole moments given earlier, and one is probably measuring complementary effects here.

A property which should correlate better with the dielectric constant is the equilibrium constant for the association into ion pairs, $K_{\text{assoc.}}$, of the tetra-alkylammonium salts. The attractive force between two ions of opposite charge, ze, separated by a distance r in a homogeneous medium of dielectric constant ϵ is given by:

$$F = \frac{z^2 e^2}{\epsilon r^2}$$

Table 1-4   Ligand field splittings for various solvents of the d levels of Ni^{2+}

Solvent	$Dq\ (cm^{-1})$	Solvent	$Dq\ (cm^{-1})$
NH$_3$	1,080	CH$_3$·CO·NH(CH$_3$)	752
H$_2$O	860	C$_6$H$_5$·CN	970
(CH$_3$)$_2$SO	773	H·CO·N(CH$_3$)$_2$	850
CH$_3$·OH	850	H·CO·NH(CH$_3$)	838
C$_5$H$_5$N	~1,000	CH$_3$·NH$_2$	993
CH$_3$·CN	1,026	C$_2$H$_5$·NH$_2$	987
CH$_3$·CO·N(CH$_3$)$_2$	769		

In a solvent two effects will occur:

1. The charge–dipole interactions of the ions with the solvent will result in a partial charge distribution over the first layer of solvent molecules round the ion. This dispersion of charge will attenuate the electric field round the ion and decrease ion pairing.

2. A high bulk dielectric constant will attenuate the electric field around the ion more rapidly than a low dielectric constant and again reduce ion pairing.

Some values of $K_{assoc.}$ for tetra-alkylammonium salts in different solvents are given in Table 1-5. For solvents with dielectric constants much above 30 the values of $K_{assoc.}$ cease to be a useful guide, but there is a wide spread of values for those solvents with values of ϵ less than 30.

A useful criterion of solvating power, proposed by Kosower, is the Z-value scale. The Z-value is the wavelength of the band maximum for the charge-transfer transition for the ion pair, 1-ethyl-4-carbomethoxypyridinium iodide, given as an energy in kcal per g-mol. Since the ground state of the ion pair is ionic, whilst the excited state to which the transition occurs is not, the energy of the ground state is lowered by a solvent of high solvating power, whilst the excited state is little affected. Consequently the Z-value will be higher in a highly polar solvent than in a non-polar solvent. There may be a fairly specific interaction with the anion in a hydrogen bonding solvent, leading to enhanced stabilization of the ground state and hence an enhanced Z-value. Table 1-6 gives Z-values for a number of solvents.

Table 1-5   Values of $K_{assoc.}$ for a variety of solvents

Solvent	Salt	$K_{assoc.}$
$CH_3 \cdot CO \cdot N(CH_3)_2$	Et_4NBr	20
	Pr_4NBr	20
$CH_3 \cdot CO \cdot NH(CH_3)$	Et_4NBr	0
	$CsBr$	0
$C_6H_5 \cdot NO_2$	Bu_4NBr	46
$(CH_3)_2CO$	Bu_4NI	164
$CH_3 \cdot OH$	Bu_4NBr	26·0
C_5H_5N	Bu_4NBr	4,000
	Bu_4NI	2,440
$CH_3 \cdot CN$	Me_4NCl	77·5
	Me_4NBr	41·4
	Me_4NI	27·5
SO_2	Me_4NCl	10,300
	Me_4NBr	11,800
	Me_4NI	13,900
	Et_4NBr	21,000

Table 1-6   Kosower Z-values for ionizing solvents

Solvent	Z-value
H_2O	94·6
$CH_3 \cdot CO \cdot N(CH_3)_2$	66·9
$CH_3 \cdot CO \cdot NH(CH_3)$	77·9
$(CH_3)_2SO$	71·1
$(CH_3)_2CO$	65·7
$CH_3 \cdot OH$	83·6
$C_2H_5 \cdot OH$	79·6
C_5H_5N	64·0
$CH_3 \cdot CN$	71·3
CH_2Cl_2	64·2
Iso-octane	60·1

Another criterion for the coordinating power of a solvent, suggested by Joesten and Drago, is the heat of formation of the phenol adduct. This measures fairly specifically the ability of the solvent to act as an electron pair donor on hydrogen bond formation. Some data are given in Table 1-7.

An alternative criterion of coordinating power is the heat of formation of the adduct with iodine. Here one is measuring the ability of the solvent to act as an electron pair donor to a very 'soft' Lewis acid.

1-4   Self-ionization of solvents

At this point it is worth discussing, in general, acid–base reactions in a solvent and self-ionization of solvents. To labour the obvious it

Table 1-7   Heats of formation of the phenol and iodine adducts for some ionizing solvent (ΔH in kcal mol^{-1})

Solvent	ΔH for phenol	ΔH for iodine
$(C_2H_5)_2O$	−5·0	—
$CH_3 \cdot CO \cdot N(CH_3)_2$	−6·4	−4·0
$CH_3 \cdot CO \cdot NH(CH_3)$	−4·7	—
$(CH_3)_2SO$	−6·5	−4·4
$CH_3 \cdot NO_2$	−1·9	—
$C_6H_5 \cdot NO_2$	−2·04	—
$(CH_3)_2CO$	−3·3	−2·5
C_5H_5N	−8·07	−7·8
$CH_3 \cdot CN$	−3·3	−2·3
$C_6H_5 \cdot CN$	−3·3	—
$CH_3 \cdot OH$	—	−1·90
$C_2H_5 \cdot OH$	—	−2·10
NH_3	−8·2	−4·8
$CH_3 \cdot NH_2$	−9·27	−7·1

must be made clear that ionizing solvents, that is, solvents capable of producing ionization in dissolved solutes, need not themselves ionize to any appreciable extent. Indeed the self-ionization of most organic solvents is negligible. However, there are two classes of solvent which do exhibit appreciable self-ionization. The first class comprises solvents with very polar bonds to a hydrogen atom— usually the more polar the bond the greater the degree of self-ionization. Thus, ammonia would be expected to exhibit a lower self-ionization than water. The most highly self-ionized solvents are the Group VI acids, sulphuric acid and selenic acid. Phosphoric acid also exhibits a very high degree of self-ionization.

Table 1-8 Auto-solvolysis constants, K_{ap}, and specific conductivities of pure solvents, L_0.

Solvent	$-log_{10} K_{ap}$	$L_0 (ohm^{-1} cm^{-1})$
NH_3	29·8	1×10^{-11}
$C_2H_5 \cdot OH$	18·9	
H_2O	14·0	
$CH_3 \cdot CO_2H$	12·6	
HF	9·7	$<10^{-6}$
H_2SO_4	3·6	$1 \cdot 0439 \times 10^{-2}$
H_3PO_4	~ 2	
$AsCl_3$	<15	$1 \cdot 4 \times 10^{-7}$
$POCl_3$	<13	2×10^{-8}
BrF_3		$8 \cdot 0 \times 10^{-3}$
ICl		$4 \cdot 6 \times 10^{-3}$

The best quantity to use to compare self-ionizations is the auto-solvolysis constant of the solvent. Unfortunately the information necessary to obtain this is not always available and one is often reduced to comparing specific conductivities of the pure solvents. A list of these for various solvents is given in Table 1-8.

The other class of solvents which shows appreciable self-ionization is very polar halides. Here the effect is often accompanied by three-centre bonding through a halogen atom bridge with a considerable increase in solvent viscosity. An example of this class is antimony pentafluoride.

Another general point that may be considered here is the possible range of acid–base strengths in a solvent. In terms of Brønsted–Lowry or protonic acids, the strongest acid in a solvent is the protonated form of that solvent and the strongest base the deprotonated form. Thus, the strongest acid in water is the H_3O^+ ion and the strongest base the OH^- ion. In liquid ammonia the NH_4^+ ion is the strongest acid and the NH_2^- ion the strongest base. The basicity of ammonia is about 10^{12} times greater than that of water and its acidity about 10^{-25} times less. Consequently, acids with a pK_a less than about 12 in water are 'strong' acids in liquid ammonia. Acetic acid is a strong acid in liquid ammonia, as is ammonium acetate.

Any solvent which accepts protons more readily than water will be a more basic solvent than water, and any solvent which donates protons to a solute more readily than water, i.e. deprotonates more readily, will be a more acid solvent than water. The smaller the self-ionization constant of the protonic solvent, the wider the range of acid strengths that may be studied in it. In Fig. 1-2 the pK_a ranges

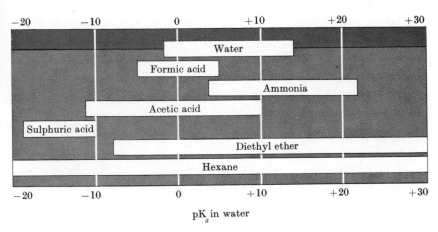

Fig. 1-2 pK_a ranges over which differentiation of acid strengths is possible in various solvents.

for which differentiation of acid strengths is possible is shown for a number of common solvents.

When one moves away from considering protonic acids and bases it is no longer possible to be so quantitative as the necessary data are not available. However, the same principles hold. Consider the Lewis acid boron trifluoride. Its strength as an acid in a solvent is determined by the strength of its complex with the solvent. In pyridine, for example, the complex $C_5H_5N \cdot BF_3$ is formed and only Lewis bases stronger than pyridine will displace pyridine from the complex. Acetonitrile will not and so is not powerful enough to function as a Lewis base in pyridine.

Again, consider the reactions of the chloride ion, a Lewis base, with the weakish Lewis acid, germanium tetrachloride. In liquid hydrogen chloride, the chloride ion interacts strongly with the solvent, via hydrogen bonds, to form the bichloride ion, HCl_2^-. Consequently, the hexachlorogermanate ion is not formed. In a solvent, such as nitromethane, that interacts less strongly with chloride ions, $GeCl_6^{2-}$ ions are formed.

Just as the properties of a solvent limit acid and base strengths to a range of values, so the properties of a solvent limit the range of oxidation potentials attainable in it and hence the range of oxidizing agents and reducing agents that can be used. Thus, in liquid ammonia, if all reactions were thermodynamically controlled (as opposed to being kinetically controlled) no oxidizing agent more powerful than nitrogen and no reducing agent more powerful than hydrogen could exist in the solvent. In acid solution the potentials of the NH_3-N_2 and H_2-NH_3 half-cell reactions are:

$$\tfrac{1}{2}H_2 + NH_3 = NH_4^+ + e^- \qquad E^0 = 0$$

$$4NH_3 = \tfrac{1}{2}N_2 + 3NH_4^+ + 3e^- \qquad E^0 = 0.04$$

and the range of potentials in basic solution is the same. With only a range of $0.04\,V$ available (compare $0.815\,V$ for pure water and

Table 1-9   Thermodynamic limits of oxidation–reduction reactions in a range of solvents

Solvent	Highest oxidized species	Lowest reduced species
NH_3	N_2	H_2
H_2O	O_2	H_2
HF	F_2	H_2
HCl	Cl_2	H_2
H_2SO_4	$H_2S_2O_8$	H_2
HSO_3F	$S_2O_6F_2$	H_2
$CH_3 \cdot OH$	H_2CO	H_2
$CH_3 \cdot COOH$	$(CH_3 \cdot CO)_2O_2$	H_2
$SbCl_3$	$SbCl_5$	$Sb(?)$
$AsCl_3$	Cl_2	As

$1.23\,V$ for aqueous acid solutions) hardly any oxidizing or reducing species would be stable in liquid ammonia. However, both the hydrogen couple and particularly the nitrogen couple show high overvoltages in the solvent, so that one can work with a range of thermodynamically unstable, but kinetically stable, oxidizing and reducing agents.

Many solvents offer a much wider thermodynamic range than liquid ammonia. Thus, in liquid hydrogen fluoride any compound with an oxidation potential below that of fluorine or above that of hydrogen would be thermodynamically stable. The oxidized and reduced species which set the upper and lower limits of thermo-dynamic stability in a variety of solvents are listed in Table 1-9.

1-5   Effect of solvent on certain types of reaction

1-5-1   Precipitation

The formation of a precipitate when solutions of two compounds are mixed is one of the most familiar chemical reactions. Such a reaction is dependent upon the solubilities of the possible products in a particular solvent, and these depend critically upon the solvation energies of the ions considered in that solvent. Hence, the precipitation reaction is highly dependent on the solvent employed.

On mixing solutions of barium chloride and silver nitrate in water, silver chloride is precipitated:

$$BaCl_2 + 2AgNO_3 \xrightarrow{\text{water}} 2AgCl\downarrow + Ba(NO_3)_2$$

However, in liquid ammonia, on mixing solutions of silver chloride and barium nitrate, it is barium chloride that is precipitated:

$$Ba(NO_3)_2 + 2AgCl \xrightarrow{NH_3(l)} BaCl_2\downarrow + 2AgNO_3$$

1-5-2   Salt formation

Here the use of the appropriate non-aqueous solvent makes possible the preparation of salts which will not form under other conditions. Thus if we wish to prepare sodium ureide, $Na^+(H_2N\cdot CO\cdot NH)^-$, we must use a base strong enough to take a proton from the very weak acid urea. In water, the strongest base available, hydroxide, will not do this and the following reaction takes place:

$$H_2N\cdot CO\cdot NH^- + H_2O \xrightarrow{\text{water}} OH^- + H_2N\cdot CO\cdot NH_2$$

However, by carrying out the reaction in liquid ammonia, a proton is readily removed from urea by the base sodium amide:

$$H_2N\cdot CO\cdot NH_2 + NH_2^- \xrightarrow{NH_3(l)} H_2N\cdot CO\cdot NH^- + NH_3$$

Another interesting example is the preparation of phosphonium salts. Phosphine is such a weak base that in water the phosphonium ion loses a proton to the solvent and phosphine evolves:

$$PH_4^+ + H_2O \xrightarrow{\text{water}} H_3O^+ + PH_3\uparrow$$

However, in the strongly acid solvent liquid hydrogen chloride, phosphine is a strong base and salts can readily be prepared:

$$PH_3 + HCl \xrightarrow{HCl(l)} PH_4^+ + Cl^-(\text{solv.}) \mid BCl_3 \longrightarrow PH_4^+BCl_4^-$$

Yet another example is the formation of the salt nitrosonium tetrachloroborate. In liquid hydrogen chloride this salt may be made

Table 1-10 Solvolytic reactions

Solvent	Auto-ionization	Solvolytic processes
H_2O	$2H_2O \rightleftharpoons H_3O^+ + OH^-$	$SOCl_2 + 4H_2O \rightarrow SO(OH)_2 + 2H_3O^+ + 2Cl^-$ $Cl_2 + 2H_2O \rightarrow HOCl + H_3O^+ + Cl^-$ $BCl_3 + 6H_2O \rightarrow H_3BO_3 + 3H_3O^+ + 3Cl^-$
NH_3	$2NH_3 \rightleftharpoons NH_4^+ + NH_2^-$	$SOCl_2 + 4NH_3 \rightarrow SO(NH_2)_2 + 2NH_4^+ + 2Cl^-$ $Cl_2 + 2NH_3 \rightarrow H_2NCl + NH_4^+ + Cl^-$ $BCl_3 + 6NH_3 \rightarrow B(NH_2)_3 + 3NH_4^+ + 3Cl^-$
$CH_3{\cdot}OH$	$2CH_3{\cdot}OH \rightleftharpoons CH_3{\cdot}OH_2^+ + CH_3{\cdot}O^-$	$SOCl_2 + 4CH_3{\cdot}OH \rightarrow SO(O{\cdot}CH_3)_2 + 2CH_3{\cdot}OH_2^+ + 2Cl^-$ $CH_3^- + CH_3{\cdot}OH \rightarrow CH_3{\cdot}O^- + CH_4$ $BCl_3 + 6CH_3{\cdot}OH \rightarrow B(O{\cdot}CH_3)_3 + 3CH_3{\cdot}OH_2^+ + 3Cl^-$
HF	$3HF \rightleftharpoons H_2F^+ + HF_2^-$	$SOCl_2 + 2HF \rightarrow SOF_2 + 2HCl\uparrow$ $PCl_5 + 5HF \rightarrow PF_5 + 5HCl\uparrow$ $H_3PO_4 + 3HF \rightarrow H_2PO_3F + H_3O^+ + HF_2^-$ $BCl_3 + 3HF \rightarrow BF_3 + 3HCl\uparrow$
H_2SO_4	$2H_2SO_4 \rightleftharpoons H_3SO_4^+ + HSO_4^-$	$B_2O_3 + 9H_2SO_4 \rightarrow 2B(HSO_4)_4^- + 3H_3O^+ + HSO_4^-$ $HNO_3 + 2H_2SO_4 \rightarrow NO_2^+ + H_3O^+ + 2HSO_4^-$ $BCl_3 + 5H_2SO_4 \rightarrow B(HSO_4)_4^- + H_3SO_4^+ + 3HCl$
BrF_3	$2BrF_3 \rightleftharpoons BrF_2^+ + BrF_4^-$	$SbCl_5 + 6BrF_3 \rightarrow BrF_2^+SbF_6^- + 5BrF + 5ClF$ $BCl_3 + 4BrF_3 \rightarrow BrF_2^+BF_4^- + 3BrF + 3ClF$

Table 1-11   Examples of solvate formation

Solvent	Solvate	Structure
NH_3	$CuSO_4 \cdot 4NH_3$	$Cu(NH_3)_4^{2+}SO_4^{2-}$
NH_3	$NH_3 \cdot BF_3$	(structure)
H_2O	$MgCl_2 \cdot 6H_2O$	$Mg(H_2O)_6^{2+}2Cl^-$
H_2O	$KOH \cdot H_2O$	$K^+(HOHOH)^-$
HF	KHF_2	$K^+(FHF)^-$
HF	KH_2F_3	K^+ (structure)
HCl	Me_4NHCl_2	$Me_4N^+(ClHCl)^-$
HCl	$Oct_4N^+H_2Cl_3^-$	Oct_4N^+ (structure)
$CH_3 \cdot COOH$	$K(OOC \cdot CH_3) \cdot CH_3 \cdot COOH$	(structure)
SO_2	$K_2SO_3 \cdot SO_2$	(structure)
	$KF \cdot SO_2$	(structure)
	$Me_4NCl \cdot SO_2$	(structure)
	$(C_2H_5)_3N \cdot SO_2$	(structure)
$(CH_3)_2SO$	$((CH_3)_2SO)_3NiCl_2$	$[(CH_3)_2SO]_6Ni^{2+} NiCl_4^{2-}$
	$[(CH_3)_2SO]_6Co(ClO_4)_2$	$[(CH_3)_2SO]_6Co^{2+}(ClO_4^-)_2$
$POCl_3$	$POCl_3, SbCl_5$	$Cl_3PO \rightarrow SbCl_5$
	$POCl_3, BCl_3$	$Cl_3PO \rightarrow BCl_3$
$AsCl_3$	$Me_4NCl, AsCl_3$	$Me_4N^+ \quad AsCl_4^-$
I_2	RbI, I_2	$Rb^+ I_3^-$
ICl	PCl_5, ICl	$PCl_4^+ ICl_2^-$
ICl_3	Me_4NCl, ICl_3	$Me_4N^+ICl_4^-$
	$SbCl_5, ICl_3$	$ICl_2^+ SbCl_6^-$
BrF_3	KF, BrF_3	$K^+ BrF_4^-$
	SbF_5, BrF_3	$BrF_2^+ SbF_6^-$

by the reaction of nitrosyl chloride, a weak base in the solvent, with boron trichloride:

$$NOCl \xrightarrow{HCl(l)} NO^+ + Cl^-(solv.) + BCl_3 \xrightarrow{HCl(l)} NO^+BCl_4^-$$

In water, of course, the exceedingly strong acid, NO^+, is unstable, reacting with the solvent to give nitrous acid:

$$NO^+ + 2H_2O \rightarrow HONO + H_3O^+$$

1-5-3 Solvolysis

A solvolytic reaction is one in which a solvent molecule reacts with the solute, splitting into two parts, one or both of which may become attached to the solute molecule. In most cases the solvolytic process results in an increase in the concentration of either the anion or the cation which is characteristic of the auto-ionization of the solvent. Solvents which do not display auto-ionization reactions are unlikely to participate in solvolysis reactions. Examples of some solvolytic processes are given in Table 1-10.

1-5-4 Solvate formation

In many instances when a solute is dissolved in a solvent and the excess of solvent removed, a solid product is recovered which contains a number of molecules of the solvent attached to a solute species (cation, anion, or neutral molecule) by any of the various types of chemical bonds, e.g. coordinate covalent, hydrogen bonding, or ion–dipole interaction. The number of molecules in the solid solvate may or may not provide a clue to the solvation number of an ion in solution. Table 1-11 gives some examples of solvate formation.

Problems

1-1 Give an account of the factors that determine the properties of an ionizing solvent and comment on the various methods that have been used to measure solvent properties.

1-2 Discuss the techniques available for the identification of the species present in solutions of inorganic solutes in non-aqueous ionizing solvents.

1-3 Give a short account of redox reactions in non-aqueous solvents.

1-4 Review critically the meaning of the terms *acid* and *base*, with special reference to phenomena in non-aqueous solvents.

1-5 In the infrared spectrum of water the O—H stretching and bending frequencies are shifted strongly by negative ions, but are virtually unaffected by positive ions. The shifts increase in magnitude along the series $I^- < Cl^- < F^-$. Comment on these observations.

1-6 Aniline is too weak a base to be titrated satisfactorily in aqueous solutions, but it can be titrated in glacial acetic acid. Comment on this.

Bibliography

1. PARKER, A. J. The effects of solvation on the properties of anions in dipolar aprotic solvents. *Q. Rev. Chem. Soc.*, 1963, **16**, 163.
2. CONWAY, B. E. and J. O'M. BOCKRIS. Ionic solvation. Chapter 2 in *Modern aspects of electrochemistry*, *Vol. I*, edited by J. O'M. BOCKRIS. Butterworths, London, 1954.
3. CONWAY, B. E. Proton solvation and proton transfer processes in solution. Chapter 2 in *Modern aspects of electrochemistry*, *Vol. III*, edited by J. O'M. BOCKRIS and B. E. CONWAY. Butterworths, London, 1964.
4. DRAGO, R. S. and K. F. PURCELL. The coordination model for non-aqueous solvent behaviour, in Vol. 6 of *Progress in inorganic chemistry*, edited by F. ALBERT COTTON. Interscience, New York, 1964.

2 Protonic solvents— water, liquid ammonia, liquid hydrogen fluoride, and sulphuric acid

Water is merely included in this chapter for comparative purposes and no detailed discussion of its properties will be given. The other three compounds are all 'good' solvents and are the most frequently used of all protonic non-aqueous solvents. It is clear from the list of physical properties of the four protonic solvents (Table 2-1) that there

Table 2-1 The physical properties of water, liquid ammonia, liquid hydrogen fluoride, and sulphuric acid

	NH_3	H_2O	HF	H_2SO_4
Melting point (°C)	$-77\cdot70$	0	$-89\cdot37$	$10\cdot371$
Boiling point (°C)	$-33\cdot38$	100	$19\cdot51$	$290\cdot317$
Liquid range (°C)	$44\cdot3$	100	109	~300
Viscosity (centipoise)	$0\cdot2543$ ($-33\cdot5$°C)	$0\cdot8904$ (25°C)	$0\cdot256$ (0°C)	$24\cdot54$ (25°C)
Density (g cm^{-3})	$0\cdot6900$ (-40°C)	$1\cdot00$ (4°C)	$1\cdot002$ (0°C)	$1\cdot8269$ (25°C)
Dielectric constant	23 ($-33\cdot4$°)	$78\cdot5$	84 (0°C)	100 (25°C)
Specific conductivity (ohm^{-1} cm^{-1})	$\sim10^{-11}$	5×10^{-7}	$\sim10^{-6}$ (0°C)	$1\cdot0439 \times 10^{-2}$
Trouton's constant	$23\cdot28$	$26\cdot0$	$24\cdot7\cdot$	
Auto-protolysis constant	$5\cdot1 \times 10^{-27}$	10^{-14} (25°C)	$\sim2 \times 10^{-12}$	$2\cdot7 \times 10^{-4}$ (25°C)

will be a wide variation in their solution properties. The dielectric constant of liquid ammonia is considerably lower than that of the other three, all of which have dielectric constants of the magnitude that one might expect for very good solvents. In consequence salts of either doubly charged anions or cations tend to be insoluble in ammonia. Magnesium, calcium, strontium, and barium salts are insoluble as are carbonates and sulphates. Both sulphuric acid and liquid hydrogen fluoride are such strong acids that the number of true salts in these systems is very limited and discussion of solubilities is limited to the hydrogen sulphates and fluorides respectively.

A property of the four solvents which it is worthwhile to compare is the equivalent ionic conductivity at infinite dilution of various ions.

This is done in Table 2-2. The data are fairly plentiful for ammonia and water, but very limited for hydrogen fluoride. In sulphuric acid the values for the positive ions are so small as not to be known accurately. However, it is clear from the data we have that, whilst in water the H_3O^+ and OH^- ions are abnormally conducting as are the F^- ion in HF and the HSO_4^- and $H_3SO_4^+$ ions in sulphuric acid, there is no abnormal conduction shown by the NH_4^+ and NH_2^- ions in liquid

Table 2-2   Equivalent ionic conductivities

	NH_3 ($-33 \cdot 5°C$)	H_2O (25°C)	H_2SO_4 (25°C)	HF (0°C)
Na^+	158	50·1	~3	
NH_4^+	142	73·5		
H_3O^+		349·8		
NO_3^-	177	71·4		
NH_2^-	166	—		
OH^-		198·3		
Br^-	170	78·2		
K^+	177	73·5	~5	120
Cl^-		76·3		
F^-		55·4		280
HSO_4^-			151·2	
$H_3SO_4^+$			152	

ammonia. This is usually explained in terms of conduction by proton tunnelling in the first three cases, a mechanism lacking in ammonia. The reason for this is probably the much weaker hydrogen bonds in this solvent. (The weaker the hydrogen bond, the higher the barrier between the two equilibrium positions for the proton.)

2-1 Liquid ammonia

There have probably been more quantitative measurements on liquid ammonia than on any other non-aqueous solvent. In general salts containing doubly charged ions are insoluble in the solvent, probably because their lattice energies are too high. Salts with highly polarizable anions tend to be more soluble than those without. Some solubilities are given in Table 2-3, from which it can be seen that the polarizable iodides and thiocyanates have a high solubility in the solvent, as have ammonium salts, possibly due to specific hydrogen bond interaction.

In general, the solubilities of covalent organic compounds in liquid ammonia are considerably higher than in water, probably owing to the greater dispersion energy interaction. These data are summarized in Table 2-4.

Table 2-3   Solubilities of salts in liquid ammonia at 25°C (g/100 g of NH_3)

Salt	Solubility	Salt	Solubility
NH_4Cl	102·5	NaBr	137·95
NH_4Br	237·9	NaI	161·9
NH_4I	368·4	NaSCN	205·5
NH_4SCN	312·0	$NaNO_3$	97·6
NH_4ClO_4	137·9	Na_2SO_4	0·0
NH_4NO_3	390·0	$NaNH_2$	0·004
$NH_4(CH_3 \cdot CO_2)$	253·2	$Ba(NO_3)_2$	97·22
$(NH_4)_2CO_3$	0·0	$BaCl_2$	0·0
$(NH_4)_2SO_3$	0·0	KCl	0·04
AgCl	0·83	KBr	13·5
AgBr	5·92	KI	182·0
AgI	206·84	KNO_3	10·4
$AgNO_3$	86·04	K_2CO_3	0·0
NaF	0·35	K_2SO_4	0·0
NaCl	3·02	KNH_2	3·6

Because of its ability to donate its lone pair of electrons to form a covalent coordinate link, as well as by ion–dipole attraction, ammonia forms many solvates. Notable for stability are those with transition metal ions—a partial list is: $Hg(NH_3)_2^{2+}$, $Pt(NH_3)_4^{2+}$, $Cu(NH_3)_4^{2+}$, $Cr(NH_3)_6^{3+}$, $Co(NH_3)_6^{3+}$, $Ni(NH_3)_6^{2+}$, $Fe(NH_3)_6^{2+}$, $Ag(NH_3)_2^{+}$, $Cu(NH_3)_2^{+}$. These ammonia solvates or ammonates are formal analogues of the corresponding aqueous compounds, the salt hydrates. They may be prepared from liquid ammonia, by the ammonation of the metal salts in aqueous ammonia, or by the action of gaseous ammonia on the anhydrous salts.

Table 2-4   Solubilities of organic compounds in liquid NH_3

Hydrocarbons Saturated aliphatic hydrocarbons are insoluble. Benzene and toluene are highly soluble.

Alcohols Aliphatic alcohols, e.g. methyl, ethyl, glycol, glycerol, are miscible with liquid ammonia in all proportions. Phenols are quite soluble.

Amines Primary > secondary > tertiary. Solubility decreases with increasing molecular weight.

Heterocyclic nitrogen bases All simple nitrogen heterocycles are quite soluble in liquid ammonia.

Esters Simple esters are highly soluble.

Ethers Diethyl ether is moderately soluble, but solubility decreases with increasing molecular weight.

Amides Simple amides are quite soluble.

2-1-1   Chemical reactions in liquid ammonia

Ammonolysis.   Some of these reactions have already been mentioned e.g.:

$$\underset{\underset{Cl}{\diagdown}}{\overset{\overset{Cl}{\diagup}}{SO_2}} + 4NH_3 \rightarrow \underset{\underset{NH_2}{\diagdown}}{\overset{\overset{NH_2}{\diagup}}{SO_2}} + 2NH_4Cl$$

Other typical ammonolytic reactions are the conversions of esters, usually requiring catalysis by NH_4^+, to amides:

$$CH_3{\cdot}C\underset{\underset{O{\cdot}C_2H_5}{\diagdown}}{\overset{\overset{O}{\diagup}}{}} + NH_3 \xrightarrow{NH_4^+} CH_3{\cdot}C\underset{\underset{NH_2}{\diagdown}}{\overset{\overset{O}{\diagup}}{}} + C_2H_5{\cdot}OH$$

The reactions of many covalent halides also fall into this category:

$$BCl_3 + 6NH_3 \rightarrow B(NH_2)_3 + 3NH_4Cl$$
$$3SiH_3Cl + 4NH_3 \rightarrow (SiH_3)_3N + 3NH_4Cl$$
$$SiCl_4 + 8NH_3 \rightarrow Si(NH_2)_4 + 4NH_4Cl$$
$$C_5H_{11}Br + NH_3 \rightarrow 10\% \ C_5H_{11}{\cdot}NH_2 + 80\% \ (C_5H_{11})_2NH$$
$$C_6H_5{\cdot}CH_2Cl + NH_3 \rightarrow 53\% \ C_6H_5{\cdot}CH_2{\cdot}NH_2 + 39\% \ (C_6H_5{\cdot}CH_2)_2NH$$

Metathetical reactions.   Some of these are straightforward neutralization reactions and may be followed by a variety of physical techniques. Thus:

$$NH_4Cl + KNH_2 \rightarrow KCl + 2NH_3$$

is entirely analogous to an acid–base reaction in water.

The saturated solution of ammonium nitrate in liquid ammonia, which has a vapour pressure of less than an atmosphere even at room temperature, is known as Diver's solution. It will dissolve potassium hydroxide and sodium hydroxide and the oxides of calcium, magnesium, zinc, cadmium, copper, and mercury to give nitrates which are soluble in - the ammonium nitrate–liquid ammonia mixture. Metals react, in many cases giving nitrites by reduction.

Ammonium salts dissolved in liquid ammonia can be used also in the syntheses of various hydrides. Thus:

$$\left.\begin{array}{c} Mg_xSi_y \\ Mg_xGe_y \end{array}\right\} + NH_4Br \rightarrow \text{high yields of } SiH_4, GeH_4$$

Sodium arsenide reacts with ammonium bromide to produce arsine:

$$Na_3As + 3NH_4Br \rightarrow AsH_3{\uparrow} + 3NaBr + 3NH_3$$

Solutions of potassium amide and other alkali metal amides in liquid ammonia may be used to produce salts of some unusual acids. Thus:

$$CH_3 \cdot C \overset{O}{\underset{NH_2}{<}} + NH_2^- \rightarrow CH_3 \cdot C \overset{O}{\underset{NH^-}{<}} + NH_3$$

Sulphamic acid, a strong monobasic acid in water, can actually be titrated as a dibasic acid in liquid ammonia:

$$SO_2 \overset{NH_2}{\underset{OH}{<}} + 2NH_2^- \rightarrow SO_2 \overset{NH^-}{\underset{O^-}{<}} + 2NH_3$$

Even acetylene may be converted into its potassium salt:

$$C_2H_2 + KNH_2 \rightarrow KC_2H + NH_3$$

Potassium amide will also precipitate metal amides, imides, or nitrides of many metals from liquid ammonia solution just as potassium hydroxide will precipitate metal hydroxides and oxides from water:

$$AgNO_3 + KNH_2 \rightarrow AgNH_2\downarrow + KNO_3$$
$$PbI_2 + 2KNH_2 \rightarrow PbNH\downarrow + 2KI + NH_3$$
$$3HgI_2 + 6KNH_2 \rightarrow Hg_3N_2\downarrow + 6KI + 4NH_3$$
$$BiI_3 + 3KNH_2 \rightarrow BiN + 3KI + 2NH_3$$

Amphoteric reactions. Just as the addition of potassium hydroxide to a solution of a zinc or aluminium salt in water first precipitates zinc hydroxide or aluminium hydroxide and then leads, on further addition of hydroxide, to the dissolution of the precipitate with formation of a complex ion:

$$ZnCl_2 + 2KOH \rightarrow Zn(OH)_2\downarrow + 2KCl$$
$$Zn(OH)_2 + 2KOH \rightarrow 2K^+ + Zn(OH)_4^{2-}$$

so, many metals show similar behaviour in liquid ammonia. Thus:

$$AgNH_2 + KNH_2 \rightarrow K[Ag(NH_2)_2]$$
$$Zn(NH_2)_2 + 2KNH_2 \rightarrow K_2[Zn(NH_2)_4]$$

2-1-2 Solutions of metals in liquid ammonia

The most unusual feature of liquid ammonia as a solvent is its power to dissolve the alkali metals and, to a lesser extent, the alkaline earth metals and aluminium. The metals dissolve to give blue solutions which when dilute have identical absorption spectra whatever the metal. The blue colour is due to the short-wavelength tail of a broad band with a peak at approximately 15,000 Å. The solutions are extremely good conductors of electricity. Highly concentrated solutions (>1 M) are bronze coloured and have conductivities nearly as high as pure metals. The equivalent conductivities of lithium, sodium, and potassium are given in Fig. 2-1.

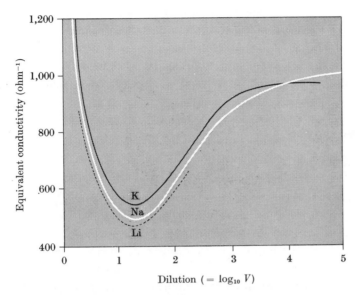

Fig. 2-1 Equivalent conductivities of metal–ammonia solutions at $-33\cdot5°C$. $V =$ litres of ammonia per g-atom of dissolved metal.

Instead of large positive temperature coefficients of conductivity, characteristic of electrolyte conduction, and owing to decrease of solvent viscosity with temperature, metal–ammonia solutions have temperature coefficients of nearly zero. Normal metals have a negative temperature coefficient of conductivity. All these metal–ammonia solutions are metastable and on long standing or in the presence of a suitable catalyst, such as iodine or ferric iodide, decompose to the amide and hydrogen:

$$2M + 2NH_3 \rightarrow H_2 + 2MNH_2$$

However, in clean apparatus with pure reagents the solutions can last for many weeks if kept at low temperatures.

The metal solutions are paramagnetic and the molar magnetic susceptibility of the solution approaches that of a mole of free electron spins, $N\mu_0^2/kT$, at infinite dilution. As the concentration is increased, however, the molar susceptibility decreases rapidly.

The conductivity of these solutions can be explained by assuming that in very dilute solutions the metal dissociates to give ammoniated cations and electrons:

$$M = M^+ + e^-$$

The electrons occupy cavities surrounded by ammonia molecules. Calculations based on the partial molar volumes of the solutes in these solutions and the partial molar volumes of K^+ and Na^+ ions give these cavities a radius of 3·34 Å. As the concentration of the solution is increased the M^+ and e^- species associate. Eventually incipient metallic behaviour occurs and the equivalent conductivity increases rapidly.

However, it is necessary to postulate other equilibria to explain the magnetic susceptibility data. These are:

$$2M^+ + 2e^- = M_2$$

and

$$M + e^- = M^-$$

When solutions of alkali metals in liquid ammonia are evaporated the free metal is recovered. However, when ammonia solutions of calcium, strontium or barium are evaporated solid phases of composition $M(NH_3)_6$ are obtained. These are excellent electrical conductors and are metallic in appearance.

Blue solutions are also obtained when solutions of tetra-alkyl-ammonium halides in liquid ammonia are cathodically reduced.

2-1-3   Reactions of metal–ammonia solutions

These solutions are strong reducing agents (stronger than hydrogen) and since many compounds are soluble in liquid ammonia the oxidation–reduction reaction is homogeneous. Reducing agents stronger than hydrogen liberate hydrogen from water and cannot generally be used in aqueous solution. Moreover, the high conductivity and strong colour of the metal–ammonia solutions mean that oxidation–reduction reactions using them can be followed both colorimetrically and conductimetrically.

The metal solutions are quickly decolorized by ammonium salts, the ammonium ion being reduced to ammonia and free hydrogen:

$$NH_4^+ + e^- \rightarrow NH_3 + \tfrac{1}{2}H_2$$

The metal solutions will also react with weakish acids, e.g. sulphamide, in liquid ammonia:

$$
\begin{array}{c}
\ce{NH_2} \\[-2pt]
\diagup \\[-4pt]
\ce{SO_2} \qquad + 2e^- \ \to\ \ce{SO_2} \qquad + \ce{H_2} \\[-4pt]
\diagdown \\[-2pt]
\ce{NH_2}
\end{array}
\qquad
\begin{array}{c}
\ce{NH^-} \\[-2pt]
\diagup \\[-4pt]
\\[-4pt]
\diagdown \\[-2pt]
\ce{NH^-}
\end{array}
$$

The simple hydrides of germanium, arsenic and phosphorus also react to give the mono-sodium derivatives:

$$\ce{GeH_4} + e^- \to \ce{GeH_3^-} + \tfrac{1}{2}\ce{H_2}$$

$$\ce{PH_3} + e^- \to \ce{PH_2^-} + \tfrac{1}{2}\ce{H_2}$$

$$\ce{AsH_3} + e^- \to \ce{AsH_2^-} + \tfrac{1}{2}\ce{H_2}$$

Most reduction reactions involving metal–ammonia solutions can be considered to belong to one of the following three types:

1. Electron addition without bond cleavage:

$$\ce{X} + e^- \to \ce{X^-}$$

An example of this type of reaction is:

$$\ce{O_2} + e^- + \ce{O_2^-}$$

and this offers a method for the preparation of pure samples of alkali metal superoxides. Further reaction between the superoxide ion and excess of metal–ammonia solutions can take place:

$$\ce{O_2^-} + e^- \to \ce{O_2^{2-}}$$

With nitrite ion:

$$\ce{NO_2^-} + e^- \to \ce{NO_2^{2-}}$$

Complex transition metal ions also can be reduced by metal–ammonia solutions:

$$\ce{MnO_4^-} + e^- \to \ce{MnO_4^{2-}}$$

$$\ce{Ni(CN)_4^{2-}} + 2e^- \to \ce{Ni(CN)_4^{4-}}$$

$$\ce{Pt(NH_3)_4^{2+}} + 2e^- \to \ce{Pt(NH_3)_4}$$

2. Bond cleavage by the addition of one electron. The reaction with the ammonium ion falls into this category:

$$\ce{NH_4^+} + e^- \to \ce{NH_3} + \tfrac{1}{2}\ce{H_2}$$

as do the reactions with other hydrides:

$$\ce{AsH_3} + e^- \to \ce{AsH_2^-} + \tfrac{1}{2}\ce{H_2}$$

and with ethanol:

$$C_2H_5 \cdot OH + e^- \rightarrow C_2H_5 \cdot O^- + \tfrac{1}{2}H_2$$

and with very weak acids.

The reaction with organic sulphides is of the same type:

$$R_2S + e^- \rightarrow RS^- + R \cdot \rightarrow RS^- + \tfrac{1}{2}R_2$$

Occasionally a stable radical is formed:

$$(C_2H_5)_3SnBr + e^- \rightarrow (C_2H_5)_3Sn \cdot + Br^-$$

3. Bond cleavage with the addition of two or more electrons. Examples of this are:

$$Ge_2H_6 + 2e^- \rightarrow 2GeH_3^-$$

$$N_2O + 2e^- \longrightarrow N_2 + O^{2-} \xrightarrow{NH_3} N_2 + OH^- + NH_2^-$$

$$NCO^- + 2e^- \longrightarrow NC^- + O^{2-} \xrightarrow{NH_3} NC^- + OH^- + NH_2^-$$

The reactions of the elements with metal–ammonia solutions probably fall into this class:

$$S_8 + ne^- \rightarrow S_2^{2-} \text{ and other polysulphides}$$

$$Se + ne^- \rightarrow Se_2^{2-} \text{ and polyselenides}$$

2-2   Liquid hydrogen fluoride

Investigations of this solvent in the past have been handicapped by its reactivity with glass and quartz. However, the advent of fluorine-containing plastics such as Teflon (polytetrafluoroethylene) and Kel-F (polychlorotrifluoroethylene) and the use of copper and stainless-steel vacuum lines have made quantitative studies easier. Most salts dissolve in the solvent with reaction and most non-ionic compounds with protonation. Even when simple fluorides are dissolved, bifluorides rather than fluorides are recovered on removal of the solvent and the fluoride ion must be heavily solvated in solution. Unlike ammonia the solvent is not particularly effective in solvating cations.

The solubilities of a range of fluorides in liquid hydrogen fluoride are given in Table 2-5. It will be seen from the table that salts with small cations are less soluble than those with large ones and that solubility decreases dramatically with increasing cation charge.

It is likely that the solubility of NbF_5, TaF_5, and SbF_5 is due to their functioning as fluoride ion acceptors in the solvent. Chlorine

Table 2-5 The solubilities of fluorides in liquid hydrogen fluoride
Data are at 12°C (unless otherwise stated) and solubilities are in g/100 g of HF

Fluoride	Solubility	Fluoride	Solubility
LiF	10·3	BeF_2	0·015
NaF	30·4	MgF_2	0·025
KF	36·5 (8°C)	CaF_2	0·87
RbF	110·0 (20°C)	SrF_2	14·83
CsF	199·0 (10°C)	BaF_2	5·60
NH_4F	32·6 (17°C)	CuF_2	0·010
AgF	83·2 (19°C)	AgF_2	0·048
TlF	580·0	PbF_2	2·62
AlF_3	<0·002	NiF_2	0·037
CeF_3	0·043	FeF_2	0·006
TlF_3	0·081	CrF_2	0·036
SbF_3	0·536	HgF_2	0·54
BiF_3	0·010	NbF_5	6·8
CeF_4	0·10	TaF_5	15·2
ThF_4	<0·006	SbF_5	Miscible in all proportions

trifluoride and bromine trifluoride are completely miscible with hydrogen fluoride and are probably acting as fluoride ion donors:

$$ClF_3 + HF \rightarrow ClF_2^+ + HF_2^-$$

The solubilities of organic covalent compounds in liquid hydrogen fluoride are extremely high and in many cases the solutions have a very high conductivity, indicating that the solute has been protonated. The reason for high solubilities is thus very different from that for ammonia. Solubilities are summarized in Table 2-6.

Table 2-6 Solubilities of organic compounds in liquid hydrogen fluoride

Hydrocarbons Saturated aliphatic hydrocarbons and their halogenated (other than fluoro) derivatives are insoluble. Aromatic hydrocarbons, such as benzene and the methylbenzenes tend to be soluble. Aromatic and aliphatic compounds are soluble if they carry substituents containing nitrogen, oxygen, or sulphur atoms.

In general the presence of electron-withdrawing groups, such as halogen or nitro on an aromatic ring, has the effect of lowering solubility. Thus, phenols are soluble, mono-nitrophenols possess only limited solubility, and trinitrophenol is insoluble. Note, however, that nitrobenzene is more soluble than benzene.

Butadiene and other unsaturated compounds polymerize.

Alcohols Aliphatic alcohols are miscible in all proportions.

Amines They are protonated to produce extremely soluble salts, as are heterocylic nitrogen bases.

Esters and ethers Protonated and very soluble.

Carboxylic acids Protonated and very soluble. Acetic acid is miscible in all proportions.

Solvates are formed exclusively by hydrogen bonding and the only ones reported are fluorides: KHF_2, KH_2F_3, KH_4F_5, and $H_3O^+H_3F_4^-$.

2-2-1 Chemical reactions in liquid hydrogen fluoride

Acid solutes, fluoride ion acceptors. Because of its high acidity, only a limited number of solutes will act as acids in liquid hydrogen fluoride. Perchloric acid and fluorosulphuric acid appear to be the only protonic acids in this category. Of the fluoride ion acceptors, antimony pentafluoride appears to be the strongest. Arsenic penta-fluoride is also very strong and solutions of these two fluorides have been shown to contain the ions SbF_6^- and AsF_6^-. Both NbF_5 and TaF_5 are also acids, though weaker than SbF_5 and AsF_5, as is PF_5. Boron trifluoride is a weak acid in the solvent with low solubility and electrical conductivity. The Group IV fluorides are essentially insoluble in liquid hydrogen fluoride.

Solvolysis reactions. Most simple salts are solvolysed, e.g.:

$$KCN + HF \rightarrow HCN\uparrow + K^+ + F^-$$
$$KCl + HF \rightarrow HCl\uparrow + K^+ + F^-$$

The initial solvolysis may be followed by a second reaction, e.g.:

$$KNO_3 + HF \rightarrow HNO_3 + K^+ + F^-$$
$$HNO_3 + HF \rightarrow H_2NO_3^+ + F^-$$
$$H_2NO_3^+ + HF \rightarrow NO_2^+ + H_3O^+ + F^-$$
$$K_2SO_4 + 2HF \rightarrow H_2SO_4 + 2K^+ + 2F^-$$
$$H_2SO_4 + HF \rightarrow HSO_3F + H_2O$$
$$H_2O + HF \rightarrow H_3O^+ + F^-$$

Acid halides and anhydrides are completely solvolysed, e.g.:

$$CH_3{\cdot}C\!\!\begin{array}{c}O\\ \diagup\!\!\diagdown\\ Cl\end{array} + HF \rightarrow HCl\uparrow + CH_3{\cdot}C\!\!\begin{array}{c}O\\ \diagup\!\!\diagdown\\ F\end{array}$$

$$(CH_3{\cdot}CO)_2O + 2HF \rightarrow CH_3{\cdot}C(OH)_2^+ + CH_3{\cdot}C\!\!\begin{array}{c}O\\ \diagup\!\!\diagdown\\ F\end{array} + F^-$$

Protonation reactions. A very wide variety of materials is protonated in HF. Indeed protonation very often follows solution.

$$CH_3{\cdot}COOH + HF \rightarrow CH_3{\cdot}C(OH)_2^+ + F^-$$
$$C_2H_5{\cdot}OH + HF \rightarrow C_2H_5{\cdot}OH_2^+ + F^-$$
$$(C_2H_5)_2O + HF \rightarrow (C_2H_5)_2OH^+ + F^-$$

Metathetical reactions. These are of minor significance in the solvent because of the extensive solvolysis which most other anions undergo in the solvent. When either HCl, HBr, or HI gas is passed through a solution of AgF or TlF in liquid hydrogen fluoride, then silver or thallium chloride, bromide, or iodide is precipitated. However, on standing without passing the gas the silver or thallium salt slowly redissolves, indicating that the first reaction is dependent on a pressure of HCl, HBr, or HI.

Silver borofluoride is precipitated when BF_3 is passed through a solution of silver fluoride in liquid hydrogen fluoride.

Amphoteric behaviour. Aluminium fluoride is relatively insoluble in liquid hydrogen fluoride, but dissolves readily on the addition of sodium fluoride:

$$AlF_3 + NaF \rightarrow Na^+ + AlF_4^-$$

The reaction is slightly more complicated than this as the actual nature of the aluminium fluoroanions present depends on the concentration of sodium fluoride. On addition of boron trifluoride, aluminium fluoride is reprecipitated:

$$NaAlF_4 + BF_3 \rightarrow AlF_3 \downarrow + NaBF_4$$

Potassium hexafluorochromate(III) is soluble in hydrogen fluoride, with precipitation of CrF_3. The precipitate redissolves in excess of sodium fluoride:

$$CrF_3 + 3NaF \rightarrow Na_3CrF_6$$

The addition of boron trifluoride causes reprecipitation of the simple fluoride:

$$Na_3CrF_6 + 3BF_3 \rightarrow CrF_3 \downarrow + 3NaBF_4$$

2-2-2   Electrochemical oxidations in liquid hydrogen fluoride

Because of the very high potential needed for the anodic reaction in liquid hydrogen fluoride:

$$F^- \rightleftharpoons \tfrac{1}{2}F_2 + e^-$$

the solvent is particularly suited to the performance of anodic oxidation reactions. These usually proceed by the insertion of fluorine in a molecule and have been widely used commercially as well as in the research laboratory for the production of fluorine-containing organic compounds. On the inorganic side the production of NFH_2,

NF_2H, and NF_3 by the electrolysis of ammonium fluoride in liquid hydrogen fluoride represents the only convenient synthetic route to these difficultly available compounds. Trifluoroacetic acid is most readily obtained by the electrolysis of acetic acid in liquid HF. When the organic starting compound is insoluble (e.g. an aliphatic hydrocarbon), soluble organic or inorganic additives are introduced to increase the conductivity and speed electrolysis. The cell container and cathode are usually made of stainless-steel and iron and the anode of nickel or platinum. Table 2-7 summarizes the products of anodic oxidation of a variety of compounds in liquid HF.

Table 2-7   Products of anodic oxidation in liquid HF

Reactant	Products
NH_4F	NF_3, NHF_2, NH_2F
H_2O	OF_2
SCl_2, SF_4	SF_6
$NaClO_4$	ClO_4F
$(CH_3)_2S$ or CS_2	CF_3SF_5, $(CF_3)_2SF_4$
$(C_2H_5)_2O$	$(C_2F_5)_2O$
$CH_3 \cdot NH_2$	$CF_3 \cdot NF_2$
$(CH_3)_2NH$	$(CF_3)_2NF$
$(CH_3)_3N$	$(CF_3)_3N$
$CH_3 \cdot CN$	$CF_3 \cdot CN$, $C_2F_5 \cdot NF_2$

2-2-3   Solutions of compounds of biological interest

Anhydrous hydrogen fluoride is a powerful solvent for polysaccharides and proteins. Cellulose dissolves freely to form conducting solutions. The material recovered from such solutions, designated a glucosan, yields glucose on mild hydrolysis.

Not only are the water-soluble proteins readily soluble in the solvent, but many fibrous proteins such as silk fibroin and collagen also dissolve freely. Although chemical reactions may occur in some cases, in many cases biological activity is retained. Insulin can be recovered from the solvent with full retention of biological activity and ribonuclease and lysozyme retain their enzymatic action after dissolution at low temperatures and recovery. The iron-containing proteins cytochrome c and haemoglobin dissolve in liquid hydrogen fluoride to form solutions with absorption spectra similar to those in water, as do the metal phthalocyanines. Vitamin B_{12} forms a deep olive-green colour in hydrogen fluoride as contrasted to its normal deep red; however, it survives solution and can be recovered with full biological activity.

2-3 Sulphuric acid

Sulphuric acid is perhaps the most extensively studied of all the strongly acidic solvents. It has a high dielectric constant and can be conveniently handled in glass apparatus at room temperature. Its only disadvantage is as a preparative solvent. If a compound is not precipitated from the solvent then removal of sulphuric acid is difficult because of its high boiling point.

Acids in the solvent give the sulphuric acidium ion, $H_3SO_4^+$, and bases the hydrogen sulphate ion, HSO_4^-. Because of its high acidity, few acids are known in the solvent and bases are much the largest class of electrolyte. Like liquid hydrogen fluoride it has a levelling effect on the strengths of bases. Despite its high acidity, sulphuric acid is also appreciably basic and this is shown by its very large auto-protolysis constant, K_{ap}, for $[H_3SO_4^+][HSO_4^-]$ which has a value of $2 \cdot 7 \times 10^{-4}$.

In addition to auto-protolysis:

$$2H_2SO_4 = H_3SO_4^+ + HSO_4^-$$

there are other dissociation equilibria which are a consequence of a primary dissociation into water and sulphur trioxide:

$$H_2SO_4 = H_2O + SO_3$$

Since water is a base in the solvent:

$$H_2O + H_2SO_4 = H_3O^+ + HSO_4^-$$

this reaction proceeds extensively to the right. Sulphur trioxide forms disulphuric acid:

$$SO_3 + H_2SO_4 = H_2S_2O_7$$

which is partly ionized as an acid:

$$H_2S_2O_7 + H_2SO_4 = H_3SO_4^+ + HS_2O_7^-$$

Since the ions $H_3SO_4^+$ and HSO_4^- are in equilibrium because of the auto-protolysis reaction, the ions H_3O^+ and $HS_2O_7^-$ must also be in equilibrium:

$$2H_2SO_4 = H_3O^+ + HS_2O_7^-$$

This has been called the ionic self-dehydration reaction, with an equilibrium constant, K_{id}. The values of the equilibrium constants are given in Table 2-8. The total molar concentration of species other than H_2SO_4 (i.e. HSO_4^-, $H_3SO_4^+$, H_3O^+, $HS_2O_7^-$, $H_2S_2O_7$, and H_2O) is $0 \cdot 0424$ M at 25°C.

Table 2-8   Self-dissociation reactions in sulphuric acid

Equation	Equilibrium constant expression	Value at 25°C
$2H_2SO_4 = H_3SO_4^+ + HSO_4^-$	$K = [H_3SO_4^+][HSO_4^-]$	$2 \cdot 7 \times 10^{-4}$
$2H_2SO_4 = H_3O^+ + HS_2O_7^-$	$K = [H_3O^+][HS_2O_7^-]$	$5 \cdot 1 \times 10^{-5}$
$H_2S_2O_7 + H_2SO_4 = H_3SO_4^+ + HS_2O_7^-$	$K = \dfrac{[H_3SO_4^+][HS_2O_7^-]}{[H_2S_2O_7]}$	$1 \cdot 4 \times 10^{-2}$
$H_2O + H_2SO_4 = H_3O^+ + HSO_4^-$	$K = \dfrac{[H_3O^+][HSO_4^-]}{[H_2O]}$	1

At atmospheric pressure, 100 % sulphuric acid has a freezing point of 10·371°C. The 100 % acid is most easily prepared by adding dilute oleum to slightly aqueous sulphuric acid until the maximum freezing point of 10·371°C is reached. Fig. 2-2 shows the freezing-point curve for the H_2O–SO_3 system in the neighbourhood of the composition H_2SO_4.

The cryoscopic constant of sulphuric acid is $6 \cdot 12 \pm 0 \cdot 02$ deg mol^{-1} kg and freezing-point depression measurements are a particularly convenient way of determining ν, the number of moles of particles (molecules or ions) produced in solution by one mole of solute. Correction has to be applied for the self-dissociated species present.

The conductivities of solutions in sulphuric acid also offer a very powerful means of determining the nature of the reaction between

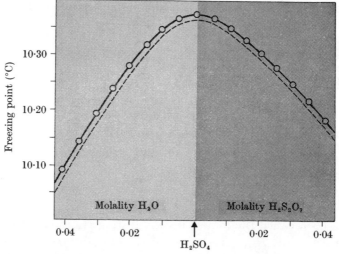

Fig. 2-2 Freezing points of sulphuric acid with added water and sulphur trioxide. The dotted line is the calculated curve, the full line is through the experimental points.

the solute and the solvent. As was pointed out earlier, the mobilities of the $H_3SO_4^+$ and HSO_4^- ions are so very much higher than those of any other ions in the solvent that the conductivities of solutions of acids and bases in sulphuric acid are determined almost entirely by the concentrations of $H_3SO_4^+$ and HSO_4^- respectively. Consequently, γ, the number of moles of HSO_4^- ions or the number of moles of $H_3SO_4^+$ ions produced by one mole of an electrolyte, can be obtained from the conductivities of any acid or base.

Some correction needs to be made at low concentrations for the repression of the solvent auto-protolysis. This is most conveniently done by comparing the concentration of a standard monohydrogen sulphate, such as $KHSO_4$, needed to produce a given conductivity with the concentration of the electrolyte under examination required to give the *same* conductivity. The ratio of the two is γ.

Table 2-9 Solubilities of metal sulphates in sulphuric acid at 25°C

Sulphate	Solubility (mole %)	Sulphate	Solubility (mole %)
Li_2SO_4	14·28	$PbSO_4$	0·12
Na_2SO_4	5·28	$CuSO_4$	0·08
K_2SO_4	9·24	$FeSO_4$	0·17
Ag_2SO_4	9·11	$NiSO_4$	very small
$MgSO_4$	0·18	$HgSO_4$	0·78
$CaSO_4$	5·16	Hg_2SO_4	0·02
$BaSO_4$	8·85	$Al_2(SO_4)_3$	<0·01
$ZnSO_4$	0·17	$Tl_2(SO_4)_3$	<0·01

Solubilities in sulphuric acid. Because of the strong hydrogen bonding between sulphuric acid molecules, it is difficult for a solute to break down the solvent structure and dissolve unless the solute is highly solvated, that is, ionic. Because of its high dielectric constant sulphuric acid is an excellent solvent for electrolytes; however, its high acidity means that most solutes dissolve with reaction. Table 2-9 gives the solubilities of a range of metal sulphates in the solvent. Those that are appreciably soluble are, of course, recovered as the bisulphate.

Most soluble sulphates are recovered from sulphuric acid as bisulphates, but this can hardly be classed as solvate formation. However, solid phases containing more sulphuric acid than this can often be prepared at low temperatures. Thus at 25°C the solid phases in equilibrium with saturated solutions in sulphuric acid are: $2LiHSO_4,H_2SO_4$; $4NaHSO_4,7H_2SO_4$; $KHSO_4,H_2SO_4$; $Mg(HSO_4)_2,2H_2SO_4$; $Ca(HSO_4)_2,2H_2SO_4$; $Ba(HSO_4)_2,2H_2SO_4$, and there is presumably strong hydrogen bonding between the bisulphate ion and the sulphuric acid in these crystal lattices.

2-3-1   Chemical reactions in sulphuric acid

Reactions in sulphuric acid are protonation, solvolysis, oxidation, or dehydration reactions. Sometimes a mixture of reactions occurs. As we have noted, there are very few strong acids in the sulphuric acid solvent system; even $H_2S_2O_7$ is relatively weak. Both conductivity and cryoscopic measurements are employed to determine the nature of the reactions.

Many aqueous acids behave as bases in sulphuric acid, e.g.:

$$CH_3 \cdot COOH + H_2SO_4 = CH_3 \cdot C(OH)_2^+ + HSO_4^- \qquad (\nu = 2;\ \gamma = 1)$$

$$H_3PO_4 + H_2SO_4 = P(OH)_4^+ + HSO_4^- \qquad (\nu = 2;\ \gamma = 1)$$

The behaviour of nitric acid is slightly more complex:

$$HNO_3 + 2H_2SO_4 = NO_2^+ + H_3O^+ + 2HSO_4^- \qquad (\nu = 4;\ \gamma = 2)$$

Presumably the protonated form of the acid, $H_2NO_3^+$, breaks down to give NO_2^+ and H_2O, which is subsequently protonated. The behaviour of hydrochloric acid in the solvent is more complex. If a chloride is dissolved in sulphuric acid there is an evolution of HCl gas, but at low concentrations in the cold HCl reacts quantitatively to give chlorosulphuric acid:

$$HCl + 2H_2SO_4 = HClSO_3 + H_3O^+ + HSO_4^- \qquad (\nu = 3;\ \gamma = 1)$$

In some cases the protonated form of a carboxylic acid, $R \cdot C(OH)_2^+$, like $H_2NO_3^+$, can lose water and give $R \cdot CO^+$. Thus:

$$R \cdot COOH + 2H_2SO_4 = R \cdot CO^+ + H_3O^+ + 2HSO_4^- \qquad (\nu = 4;\ \gamma = 2)$$

An example of an acid which undergoes this type of ionization to yield a stable acyl ion is mesitoic acid, $(CH_3)_3C_6H_2 \cdot COOH$, which gives $(CH_3)_3C_6H_2 \cdot CO^+$. On dilution with water, mesitoic acid is recovered and on dilution with methanol the methyl ester is obtained.

A number of carboxylic acids are unstable in sulphuric acid and decompose to give carbon monoxide, presumably via the acyl ion, $R \cdot CO^+$:

$$R \cdot CO^+ = R^+ + CO$$

Examples are formic acid:

$$H \cdot COOH + H_2SO_4 = CO + H_3O^+ + HSO_4^-$$

and oxalic acid:

$$(COOH)_2 + H_2SO_4 = CO + CO_2 + H_3O^+ + HSO_4^-$$

Strong acids are produced in sulphuric acid by dissolving either boric acid or boric oxide in the solvent:

$$H_3BO_3 + 6H_2SO_4 = B(HSO_4)_4^- + 3H_3O^+ + 2HSO_4^- \quad (\nu = 6; \gamma = 2)$$
$$B_2O_3 + 9H_2SO_4 = 2B(HSO_4)_4^- + 3H_3O^+ + HSO_4^- \quad (\nu = 6; \gamma = 1)$$

Solutions of the free acid can be prepared by dissolving boric acid or boric oxide in oleum instead of in sulphuric acid, in which case the H_3O^+ ion is removed by the reaction:

$$H_3O^+ + SO_3 = H_3SO_4^+$$

A solution of $HB(HSO_4)_4$ can be titrated conductimetrically with a solution of a strong base such as $KHSO_4$.

Both tin tetra-acetate and lead tetra-acetate dissolve in sulphuric acid to give acids:

$$Sn(OAc)_4 + 8H_2SO_4 = Sn(HSO_4)_6^{2-} + 4CH_3 \cdot C(OH)_2^+ + 2HSO_4^-$$
$$Pb(OAc)_4 + 8H_2SO_4 = Pb(HSO_4)_6^{2-} + 4CH_3 \cdot C(OH)_2^+ + 2HSO_4^-$$

Neither of these acids is very strong and in the case of hexa(hydrogen sulphato)plumbic acid the variation of ν and γ with concentration in the above reaction has been used to determine the two dissociation constants of the acid:

$$H_2Pb(HSO_4)_6 + H_2SO_4 = H_3SO_4^+ + HPb(HSO_4)_6^-$$
$$K_1 = 1 \cdot 2 \times 10^{-2} \, \text{mol kg}^{-1}$$
$$HPb(HSO_4)_6^- + H_2SO_4 = H_3SO_4^+ + Pb(HSO_4)_6^{2-}$$
$$K_2 = 1 \cdot 8 \times 10^{-3} \, \text{mol kg}^{-1}$$

and the acid is of about the same strength as $H_2S_2O_7$. A summary of the strengths of various acids in sulphuric acid is given in Table 2-10.

Table 2-10   Acid strengths in sulphuric acid

Acid	Ionization constant (mol kg^{-1})
$H_2S_2O_7$	$1 \cdot 4 \times 10^{-2}$
HSO_3F	3×10^{-3}
$H_2Pb(HSO_4)_6$	$1 \cdot 2 \times 10^{-2}$
$HPb(HSO_4)_6^-$	$1 \cdot 8 \times 10^{-3}$
$HB(HSO_4)_4$	4×10^{-1}
$HClO_4$	very weak
HSO_3Cl	very weak

Most ketones, aldehydes, carboxylic acids, ethers, amines, and amides are strong bases in sulphuric acid, as are organic phosphines. However, in some cases further reaction can occur. Amides appear to protonate on the oxygen rather than on the nitrogen:

$$R \cdot CO \cdot NH_2 + H_2SO_4 = R \cdot C(OH) \cdot NH_2^+ + HSO_4^-$$

and this protonation is followed by a slow solvolysis:

$$R \cdot C(OH) \cdot NH_2^+ + 2H_2SO_4 = R \cdot CO_2H_2^+ + NH_4^+ + HS_2O_7^-$$

Ethers are monoprotonated in sulphuric acid:

$$R \cdot O \cdot R' + H_2SO_4 = \begin{array}{c} R \\ \diagdown \\ \diagup \\ R' \end{array} OH^+ + HSO_4^-$$

but again the reaction is followed by a slow solvolysis:

$$\begin{array}{c} R \\ \diagdown \\ \diagup \\ R' \end{array} OH^+ + 2H_2SO_4 = RHSO_4 + R'HSO_4 + H_3O^+$$

When triphenylmethanol is dissolved in sulphuric acid it ionizes according to the equation:

$$(C_6H_5)_3C \cdot OH + 2H_2SO_4 = (C_6H_5)_3C^+ + H_3O^+ + 2HSO_4^-$$
$$(\nu = 4; \ \gamma = 2)$$

giving a stable yellow solution.

Stable carbonium ions can also be prepared by dissolving some substituted alkenes in sulphuric acid:

$$(C_6H_5)_2C{:}CH_2 + H_2SO_4 = (C_6H_5)_2C \cdot CH_3^+ + HSO_4^- \qquad (\nu = 2; \ \gamma = 1)$$

A number of inorganic and organic compounds function as weak bases in sulphuric acid. Thus, selenium dioxide is soluble in sulphuric acid to give a bright yellow solution, and in dilute solutions it behaves as a weak base:

$$SeO_2 + H_2SO_4 = HSeO_2^+ + HSO_4^-$$

though in view of the solubility the equilibrium probably ought to be written:

$$SeO_2 + H_2SO_4 = SeO(OH) \cdot HSO_4 = SeO \cdot OH^+ + HSO_4^-$$

Some organic compounds, notably nitro compounds, sulphones, and sulphoxides, are weak bases in sulphuric acid. Surprisingly, so are nitriles, the base strengths of which one would have expected to be greater, though here protonation is complicated by slow solvolysis:

$$R \cdot CN + H_2SO_4 = R \cdot CNH^+ + HSO_4^-$$
$$R \cdot CNH^+ + HSO_4^- = R \cdot CO \cdot NH_2 + SO_3$$

The ionization constants of some weak bases are given in Table 2-11.

Table 2-11 Ionization constants of weak bases in sulphuric acid

Base	$K_{ionization}$ $(mol\ kg^{-1})$
$CH_3 \cdot NO_2$	$2 \cdot 5 \times 10^{-3}$
$C_6H_5 \cdot NO_2$	$1 \cdot 0 \times 10^{-2}$
$p\text{-}MeC_6H_4 \cdot NO_2$	$9 \cdot 6 \times 10^{-2}$
$CH_3 \cdot CN$	$1 \cdot 6 \times 10^{-1}$
$C_6H_5 \cdot CN$	$7 \cdot 0 \times 10^{-2}$
$(C_6H_5)_2SO$	$1 \cdot 6 \times 10^{-2}$
SeO_2	$4 \cdot 4 \times 10^{-3}$

Problems

2-1 Give a brief account of the use of conductivity and freezing-point measurements in sulphuric acid solutions to determine the mode of ionization of the solute. The following ν (number of particles from freezing-point depression) and γ (ratio of conductivity to that of $KHSO_4$) values were found for the following compounds in solution in H_2SO_4:

Compound	ν	γ
N_2O_4	6	3
KH_2PO_4	4	2
$Pb(OAc)_4$	7	2
H_3BO_3	6	2
$NaNO_2$	6	3
$K_4P_2O_7$	12	5

Give equations for the modes of ionization of these compounds.

2-2 Give a brief account of the evidence for abnormal mobilities of certain ions in protonic solvents. What mechanism has been proposed to account for this? How would you attempt to rationalize the occurrence of abnormal mobilities in some solvents and not in others?

2-3 Give an account of the chemical properties of solutions of alkali metals in liquid ammonia. Summarize the evidence about the nature of the species present in these solutions.

2-4 A liquid-ammonia solution of phenolphthalein is colourless, but becomes intensely red on addition of KNH_2. Explain this.

2-5 In each of the following cases write down the corresponding compound in the 'nitrogen system of compounds' (e.g. $NH_4^+Cl^-$ for $H_3O^+Cl^-$ and KNH_2 for KOH): H_2O_2; $HOCl$; HNO_3; $CH_3 \cdot OH$; $Ni(H_2O)_6Cl_2$. Discuss the position of urea, sulphamic acid, and hydroxylamine in such a system.

Bibliography

1. JOLLY, W. L. and C. J. HALLADA. Liquid ammonia. Chapter 1 in *Non-aqueous solvent systems*, edited by T. C. WADDINGTON. Academic Press, London and New York, 1965.
2. WATT, G. Reactions of inorganic substances with solutions of metals in liquid ammonia. *Chem. Rev.*, 1950, **46**, 289.
3. FOWLES, G. W. A. and D. NICHOLLS. Inorganic reactions in liquid ammonia. *Q. Rev. chem. Soc.*, 1962, **16**, 19.
4. GILLESPIE, R. J. and E. A. ROBINSON. The sulphuric acid solvent system, in *Advances in inorganic chemistry and radiochemistry, Vol. 1*, edited by H. J. EMELÉUS and A. G. SHARPE. Academic Press, New York, 1959.
5. GILLESPIE, R. J. and E. A. ROBINSON. Sulphuric acid. Chapter 4 in *Non-aqueous solvent systems*, edited by T. C. WADDINGTON. Academic Press, London and New York, 1965.
6. SIMONS, J. H. Hydrogen fluoride, in *Fluorine chemistry, Vol. 1*, edited by J. H. SIMONS. Academic Press, New York, 1950.
7. HYMAN, H. H. and J. J. KATZ. Liquid hydrogen fluoride. Chapter 2 in *Non-aqueous solvents*, edited by T. C. WADDINGTON. Academic Press, London and New York, 1965.

Liquid oxide solvents—dinitrogen tetroxide and sulphur dioxide

In this chapter two solvents, dinitrogen tetroxide and sulphur dioxide, which contain no hydrogen atoms and for which it is best to use the Lewis definition of acids and bases (acids as electron pair acceptors; bases as electron pair donors), are discussed.

3-1 Liquid dinitrogen tetroxide

The physical properties of N_2O_4 are listed in Table 3-1. As would be

Table 3-1 Physical properties of liquid N_2O_4

Melting point (°C)	−12·3
Boiling point (°C)	21·3
Liquid range (°C)	33·6
Density (g cm^{-3})	1·49
Dielectric constant	2·42 (18°C)
Specific conductivity (ohm^{-1} cm^{-1})	2·36 × 10^{-13} (17°C)

expected from its very low dielectric constant, N_2O_4 is a poor solvent for ionic substances, solubilities being similar to solubilities in ether. Many organic solutes dissolve in N_2O_4 without change. Alkanes, aromatic hydrocarbons, halo and nitro compounds, and carboxylic acids are readily soluble. Many oxygen and nitrogen compounds are also soluble, for example ethers, esters and tertiary amines, and oxygen- and nitrogen-containing heterocylic compounds. Many other organic compounds containing an active hydrogen atom, such as primary and secondary amines, alcohols, and ketones, dissolve with reaction.

The proposed auto-ionization reaction in the liquid:

$$N_2O_4 \rightleftharpoons NO^+ + NO_3^-$$

must occur to an exceedingly small extent since the specific electrical conductivity of the purified liquid is so low. If this auto-ionization is correct then compounds giving the NO^+ group would be acids in the solvent and substances giving NO_3^- ions would be bases. Thus, compounds such as NOCl and NOBr will behave as acids, and nitrates such as $Et_4N^+NO_3^-$ will behave as bases. A solution of NOCl in liquid N_2O_4 will react with solid $AgNO_3$:

$$NOCl + AgNO_3(s) \xrightarrow{\ N_2O_4(l)\ } AgCl(s) + N_2O_4$$

but the same reaction will proceed equally well if NOCl is dissolved in benzene or petroleum ether.

A wide variety of transition metal nitrates form solvates with N_2O_4 and some of these are listed in Table 3-2, together with their probable structures:

Table 3-2   Solvates with N_2O_4

Salt	Solvate	Probable formulation
$Zn(NO_3)_2$	$Zn(NO_3)_2,2N_2O_4$	$(NO^+)_2[Zn(NO_3)_4^{2-}]$
$Fe(NO_3)_3$	$Fe(NO_3)_3,N_2O_4$	$NO^+[Fe(NO_3)_4^-]$
$Cu(NO_3)_2$	$Cu(NO_3)_2,N_2O_4$	$NO^+[Cu(NO_3)_3^-]$
$UO_2(NO_3)_2$	$UO_2(NO_3)_2,N_2O_4$	$NO^+[UO_2(NO_3)_3^-]$

A wide range of covalent compounds, particularly organic Lewis bases, also form adducts with N_2O_4. Boron trifluoride forms a complex $N_2O_4,2BF_3$ which has the structure:

$$NO_2^+ \ N \begin{array}{l} \diagup OBF_3^- \\[4pt] \diagdown OBF_3 \end{array}$$

an indication of an unusual ionization of the solvent molecule. A list of the adducts formed between N_2O_4 and organic molecules is given in Table 3-3. It will be seen from this table that the stability of these adducts varies greatly, and the fact that many of them are 1:1 adducts between the electron pair base and N_2O_4 is an indication that their structures may be described as:

With stronger bases, including possibly the sulphoxides and certainly the tertiary amines, the structure is ionic. Thus, trimethylamine forms the salt $(CH_3)_3NNO^+NO_3^-$.

Table 3-3   Adducts of N_2O_4 with organic molecules

Organic compound	Adduct composition	Melting point (°C)	Stability
$(C_2H_5)_2O$	$2(C_2H_5)_2O,N_2O_4$	-74.8	Very low
Tetrahydrofuran	$(CH_2)_4O_2,N_2O_4$	-20.5	Moderate
$(CH_3)_2NNO$	$2(CH_3)_2NNO,N_2O_4$	$+3$	Moderate
$CH_3 \cdot COOH$	$2CH_3 \cdot COOH,N_2O_4$	$+2$	Moderate
$C_6H_5 \cdot COOC_2H_5$	$2C_6H_5 \cdot COOC_2H_5,N_2O_4$	-13	Moderate
$(CH_3)_2CO$	$2(CH_3)_2CO,N_2O_4$	-40	Low
$(CH_3)_2SO$	$(CH_3)_2SO,N_2O_4$	$+38$	Stable
$(C_2H_5)_2SO$	$(C_2H_5)_2SO,N_2O_4$	$+14$	Stable
C_6H_6	C_6H_6,N_2O_4	-7	Moderate
Mesitylene	$C_6H_3(CH_3)_3,N_2O_4$	-18	Low
$C_6H_5 \cdot CN$	$C_6H_5 \cdot CN,N_2O_4$	-26	Low

Salts such as alkylammonium halides have a sufficiently low lattice energy to be soluble. They undergo solvolysis in the solvent:

$$Et_4NCl + N_2O_4 \rightarrow NOCl + Et_4NNO_3$$

The degree of solvolysis depends on the solubility of the chloride in the solvent. Other solvolysis reactions are:

$$Mg(OH_2)_6^{2+}(Cl^-)_2 + 2N_2O_4 \rightarrow Mg(OH_2)_6^{2+}(NO_3^-)_2 + 2NOCl$$

$$Mg(ClO_4)_2 + 2N_2O_4 \rightarrow Mg(NO_3)_2 + 2NOClO_4$$

3-1-1   Reactions of metals

Metals such as lithium and sodium react with liquid N_2O_4, e.g.:

$$Li + N_2O_4 \rightarrow NO\uparrow + MNO_3$$

The addition of nitrosyl chloride increases the reactivity of the solvent towards metals. Zinc, iron, and tin react readily with solutions of $NOCl$,:

$$Zn + 2NOCl \rightarrow ZnCl_2 + 2NO\uparrow$$

Some metals such as zinc and aluminium are amphoteric in the solvent, and though zinc only reacts slowly with pure liquid N_2O_4 it will react readily with nitrate solutions in the solvent:

$$Zn + 4(Et_2NH_2)NO_3 + 2N_2O_4 \rightarrow (Et_2NH_2)_2Zn(NO_3)_4 + 2NO\uparrow$$

$$Al + 4(Et_2NH_2)NO_3 + 3N_2O_4 \rightarrow (Et_2NH_2)Al(NO_3)_4 + 3NO\uparrow$$

Zinc nitrate, which forms the adduct $(NO^+)_2Zn(NO_3)_4^{2-}$ in the solvent, reacts with soluble nitrates to give tetranitratozincates:

$$Zn(NO_3)_2 + 2Et_2NH_2NO_3 \rightarrow (Et_2NH_2)_2Zn(NO_3)_4$$

3-2   Liquid sulphur dioxide

The physical properties of liquid sulphur dioxide are listed in Table
3-4. In general, covalent substances are considerably more soluble

Table 3-4   Some physical properties of sulphur dioxide

Melting point (°C)	-75.46
Boiling point (°C)	-10.02
Liquid range (°C)	65.5
Viscosity of liquid (millipoise)	4.285 ($-10°C$)
Dielectric constant	15.4 ($0°C$)
Specific conductivity (ohm^{-1} cm^{-1})	$3–4 \times 10^{-8}$ ($-10°C$)
Trouton's constant	22.7
Dipole moment (Debye)	1.62
Enthalpy of fusion (kcal mol^{-1})	1.97
Enthalpy of vaporization (kcal mol^{-1})	5.96

that ionic compounds in liquid sulphur dioxide. However, its higher
dielectric constant means that it is a much better solvent for ionic
compounds than liquid N_2O_4. The solubilities of some salts are given
in Table 3-5. From this table it can be seen that only the alkali metal

Table 3-5   Solubilities of alkali metal, ammonium, silver, and thallous salts in
liquid SO_2

Ion	SO_3^{2-}	SO_4^{2-}	F$^-$	Cl$^-$	Br$^-$	I$^-$	SCN$^-$	CN$^-$	ClO$_4^-$	CH$_3$·COO$^-$
Li$^+$	—	1·55	23·0	2·82	6·0	1,490·0	—	—	—	3·48
Na$^+$	1·37	insol.	6·9	insol.	1·36	1,000·0	80·5	3·67	—	8·90
K$^+$	1·58	insol.	3·1	5·5	40·0	2,490·0	502·0	2·62	—	0·61
Rb$^+$	1·27	—	—	27·2	sol.	sol.	—	—	—	—
Cs$^+$	—	—	—	—	—	—	—	—	—	—
NH$_4^+$	2·67	5·07	less than 27 at 50°C	1·67	6·0	580·0	6,160·0	—	2·14	141·0
Tl$^+$	4·96	0·417	insol.	0·292	0·60	1·81	0·915	0·522	0·43	285·0
Ag$^+$	insol.	insol.	insol.	20·07	0·159	0·68	0·845	1·42	—	1·02

Data refer to 0°C unless otherwise stated. Solubilities are in millimoles per 1,000 g of
sulphur dioxide.

iodides are soluble to the extent of more than a mole per thousand
grammes of solvent. The solubility of most of the others is only a few
millimoles. All the tetramethylammonium halides are freely soluble
in the solvent, because of their low lattice energies.

Bromine, chlorine, iodine monochloride, thionyl chloride, boron
trichloride, carbon disulphide, phosphorous trichloride, arsenic trichloride, and phosphorus oxychloride are miscible in all proportions.
Liquid sulphur dioxide is an excellent solvent for organic compounds.
Amines, ethers, esters, alcohols, sulphides, mercaptans, and acids

(both aliphatic and aromatic) are readily soluble. Aromatic hydrocarbons and alkenes dissolve readily, but paraffins have a low solubility. Water is soluble but not completely miscible with liquid sulphur dioxide.

Sulphur dioxide forms stable solvates with many alkali metal halides and other ionic compounds. The molar ratio of SO_2 to halide generally varies from one to four. Some results are summarized in Table 3-6. The mono-adducts are probably best regarded as halo-

Table 3-6   Solvate formation with alkali metal and tetramethylammonium salts

$LiI,2SO_2$	KF,SO_2	RbF,SO_2	Me_4NF,SO_2
$NaI,2SO_2$			Me_4NCl,SO_2
$NaI,4SO_2$	$KBr,4SO_2$	$RbI,4SO_2$	$CsI,4SO_2$ $Me_4NCl,2SO_2$
$NaNCS,2SO_2$	$KI,4SO_2$		Me_4NBr,SO_2
$NaCH_3 \cdot CO_2,SO_2$	$KNCS,SO_2$		$Me_4NBr,2SO_2$
	$KCH_3 \cdot CO_2,SO_2$ $RbCH_3 \cdot CO_2,SO_2$		Me_4NI,SO_2
			$(Me_4N)_2SO_4,3SO_2$
			$(Me_4N)_2SO_4,6SO_2$

sulphinites, with structure

by comparison with the halosulphonates. Their stability decreases in the order $F > Cl > Br > I$. The structure of the polysolvates has not been determined, but the iodides are here the most stable and coordination is probably through the sulphur atom to the anion.

With covalent compounds many SO_2 solvates are formed. In most cases the molecule acts as an electron acceptor through sulphur and only in a few as an electron donor through oxygen. These latter seem to be restricted to only the most powerful Lewis acids and even then are not very stable. Examples are SO_2,BF_3, SO_2,SbF_5 (the most stable), $SO_2,SnBr_4$, and $SO_2,AlCl_3$.

Organic amines form stable mono-adducts with SO_2; these compounds are usually highly coloured and coordination appears to be through the nitrogen to the sulphur. The claim of Jander and co-workers that a further reaction takes place:

$$2(C_2H_5)_3NSO_2 \rightarrow [(C_2H_5)_3N]_2SO^{2+}+SO_3^{2-}$$
$$\text{red} \qquad\qquad\qquad \text{white}$$

has now been shown to be wrong. Their solvent was wet and the white compound they isolated was $(C_2H_5)_3NH^+HSO_3^-$. A list of molecular addition compounds is given in Table 3-7.

Table 3-7   Molecular addition compounds
of SO_2

Compound	Adduct
$(CH_3)_3N$	$(CH_3)_3N,SO_2$
$(C_2H_5)_3N$	$(C_2H_5)_3N,SO_2$
$C_6H_5 \cdot N(CH_3)_2$	$C_6H_5 \cdot N(CH_3)_2,SO_2$
$C_6H_5 \cdot NH_2$	$C_6H_5 \cdot NH_2,SO_2$
Pyridine	C_5H_5N,SO_2
$p\text{-}C_6H_4(NH_2)_2$	$p\text{-}C_6H_4(NH_2)_2,2SO_2$
$(C_2H_5)_3NO$	$(C_2H_5)_3NO,SO_2$
Ethylene oxide	$(CH_2)_2O,SO_2$
Dioxane	$O(CH_2 \cdot CH_2)_2O,2SO_2$
$C_6H_5 \cdot O \cdot CH_3$	$C_6H_5 \cdot O \cdot CH_3,SO_2$
$CH_3 \cdot COOH$	$CH_3 \cdot COOH,SO_2$
$(C_2H_5)_2S$	$(C_2H_5)_2S,SO_2$

3-2-1   Electrolytic behaviour of solutions in liquid sulphur dioxide

Nearly all the experimental work in liquid sulphur dioxide is limited to uni-univalent electrolytes. These solutions are nothing like as good electrical conductors as liquid ammonia solutions or aqueous solutions. Because SO_2 is a solvent·of low dielectric constant, equilibria exist in solution not only between ions and ion pairs (uncharged) but also in more concentrated solutions between ion pairs and ion triplets (charged). A plot of equivalent conductivity against concentration shows a minimum. At concentrations above about 0·1 M the conductivity is largely due to ion triplets; a minimum is found at about 0·1 M, and below this the equivalent conductivity increases with decreasing concentration, obeying Ostwald's dilution law. Triple ion formation can be disregarded at concentrations below 0·01 M, and at this concentration association constants for ion pair formation may be determined.

The data for a number of salts at 0°C are given in Table 3-8. The limiting conductivities of the salts in the table show that there must be considerable hydrodynamic transport of solvent associated with the lithium ion. With constant cation the association constants increase from $Cl^- < Br^- < I^-$, and with constant anion they increase from $Li^+ < Na^+ < K^+ < Me_4N^+ < Et_4N^+$.

Triphenylchloromethane and some of its chloro and methyl derivatives are moderately good conductors in liquid SO_2. The conductivity results may be explained in terms of the following reactions:

$$(C_6H_5)_3CCl \rightleftharpoons (C_6H_5)_3C^+Cl^- \rightleftharpoons (C_6H_5)_3C^+ + Cl^-$$
$$\text{ion pair}$$

Table 3-8   Conductivity and ion pair association data in liquid sulphur dioxide

Ion pair	Limiting molar conductance ($cm^2\ ohm^{-1}\ mol^{-1}$)	K ($mol\ l^{-1} \times 10^4$)
LiBr	189	0·27
NaBr	265	0·48
KCl	243	0·74
KBr	249	1·43
KI	244	3·0
Me_4NCl	243	10·3
Me_4NBr	236	11·8
Me_4NI	234	13·9
Me_4NClO_4	218	8·4
Me_4NBF_4	215	7·9
Et_4NBr	215	21
Et_4NI	197	39

with an equilibrium constant:

$$K = \frac{[(C_6H_5)_3C^+][Cl^-]}{\underset{\text{ion pair}}{[(C_6H_5)_3CCl] + [(C_6H_5)_3C^+Cl^-]}}$$

Values of K for this equilibrium constant for a number of triphenyl-chloromethanes are given in Table 3-9.

Solutions of trisubstituted hydronium salts in the solvent are also fairly good electrical conductors. Salts like $(CH_3)_3O^+BF_4^-$, $(C_2H_5)_3O^+BF_4^-$, and $(C_2H_5)_3O^+SbCl_6^-$ have conductivities of about the same order of magnitude as solutions of KI. It is also worth noting that, though neither water nor hydrogen bromide by themselves are electrical conductors in sulphur dioxide, a mixture of both gives a conducting solution in the solvent, presumably due to $H_3O^+Br^-$.

Table 3-9   Values of K for triphenylchloro-methanes

Compound	K ($mol\ l^{-1} \times 10^4$)
$(C_6H_5)_3CCl$	0·415
$(o\text{-}ClC_6H_4)(C_6H_5)_2CCl$	0·106
$(m\text{-}ClC_6H_4)(C_6H_5)_2CCl$	0·0153
$(p\text{-}ClC_6H_4)(C_6H_5)_2CCl$	0·126
$(p\text{-}ClC_6H_4)_3CCl$	0·0122
$(o\text{-}CH_3{\cdot}C_6H_4)(C_6H_5)_2CCl$	6·25
$(m\text{-}CH_3{\cdot}C_6H_4)(C_6H_5)_2CCl$	0·95
$(p\text{-}CH_3{\cdot}C_6H_4)(C_6H_5)_2CCl$	7·7

3-2-2   Chemical reactions in liquid sulphur dioxide

Solvolysis reactions. Zinc diethyl reacts even at dry ice temperatures to give diethyl sulphoxide and zinc oxide:

$$Zn(C_2H_5) + SO_2 \rightarrow ZnO + (C_2H_5)_2SO$$

Ammonium acetate is also solvolysed in liquid SO_2:

$$2NH_4(CH_3 \cdot CO_2) + 2SO_2 \rightarrow (NH_4)_2SO_3 + (CH_3 \cdot CO_2)_2SO$$

$$(CH_3 \cdot CO_2)_2SO \rightarrow (CH_3 \cdot CO)_2O + SO_2$$

There is some dispute as to whether solutions of alkali metal bromides and iodides are slowly solvolysed in the solvent. Jander (1949) reported the following sequence of reactions:

$$8KBr + 8SO_2 \rightarrow 4K_2SO_3 + 4SOBr_2$$

$$4SOBr_2 \rightarrow 2SO_2 + S_2Br_2 + 3Br_2$$

$$\underline{4K_2SO_3 + 2Br_2 \rightarrow 2K_2SO_4\downarrow + 4KBr + 2SO_2}$$

$$4KBr + 4SO_2 \rightarrow 2K_2SO_4\downarrow + S_2Br_2 + Br_2$$

Presumably the same reactions take place with KI, except that S_2I_2 breaks down to sulphur and iodine:

$$4KI + 4SO_2 = 2K_2SO_4\downarrow + 2S\downarrow + 2I_2$$

However, Lichtin has reported recently (1963) that dilute solutions of bromides and iodides are quite stable when prepared in *dry* SO_2 which has been degassed (i.e. oxygen removed), and that, at least for the iodides, instability is associated with the presence of oxygen.

The behaviour of the binary halides in liquid sulphur dioxide varies. Halides of Group IV do not react. Phosphorus pentachloride and pentabromide are readily solvolysed, even at low temperatures:

$$PCl_5 + SO_2 \rightarrow POCl_3 + SOCl_2$$

$$PBr_5 + SO_2 \rightarrow POBr_3 + SOBr_2$$

Further solvolysis does not occur. This is because, though the reaction to the oxyhalide is exothermic, the further solvolysis:

$$2POCl_3 + 3SO_2 \rightarrow (P_2O_5) + 3SOCl_2$$

would represent an endothermic reaction. Other solvolytic reactions which do occur are:

$$NbCl_5 + SO_2 \rightarrow NbOCl_3 + SOCl_2$$

$$WCl_6 + SO_2 \rightarrow WOCl_4 + SOCl_2$$

$$UCl_6 + 2SO_2 \rightarrow UO_2Cl_2 + 2SOCl_2$$

Metathetical reactions. A large number of reactions, which have been called 'neutralization reactions' or 'acid–base reactions', are probably better described as metathetical reactions. Thus, sulphites react with thionyl halides in the solvent to produce chlorides and sulphur dioxide:

$$Cs_2SO_3 + SOCl_2 \rightarrow 2CsCl + 2SO_2$$
$$[Me_4N]_2SO_3 + SOBr_2 \rightarrow 2Me_4NBr + 2SO_2$$

Acetates also react:

$$2Ag(CH_3 \cdot CO_2) + SOCl_2 \rightarrow 2AgCl\downarrow + SO(CH_3 \cdot CO_2)_2$$
$$2NH_4(CH_3 \cdot CO_2) + SOCl_2 \rightarrow 2NH_4Cl\downarrow + SO(CH_3 \cdot CO_2)_2$$

$SO(CH_3 \cdot CO_2)_2$ has not been isolated; it appears to break up into acetic anhydride and sulphur dioxide. However, $(C_6H_5 \cdot CH_2 \cdot CO_2)_2SO$ and $(ClCH_2 \cdot CO_2)_2SO$ have been isolated from similar reactions. Ammonium thiocyanate also reacts with thionyl chloride:

$$2NH_4SCN + SOCl_2 \rightarrow 2NH_4Cl\downarrow + SO(SCN)_2$$

The $SO(SCN)_2$ is stable in dilute solution and can be titrated conductimetrically with K_2SO_3:

$$K_2SO_3 + SO(SCN)_2 \rightarrow 2KSCN + 2SO_2$$

The titration curve is shown in Fig. 3-1.

Amphoteric reactions. A number of reactions in liquid sulphur dioxide appear to be analogous to the behaviour of amphoteric substances in water. When a solution of tetramethylammonium sulphite

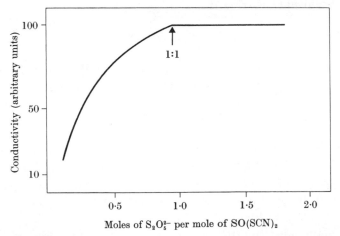

Fig. 3-1 Conductivity titration of $SO(SCN)_2$ against sulphite.

is added to a solution of aluminium chloride in liquid sulphur dioxide, a voluminous white precipitate of aluminium sulphite is formed:

$$2AlCl_3 + 3(Me_4N)_2SO_3 \rightarrow Al_2(SO_3)_3\downarrow + 6Me_4NCl$$

If an excess of tetramethylammonium sulphite is then added the precipitate redissolves, presumably with formation of a complex anion:

$$Al_2(SO_3)_3 + 3(Me_4N)_2SO_3 \rightarrow 2(Me_4N)_3Al(SO_3)_3$$

If thionyl chloride is now added to this solution the aluminium sulphite is reprecipitated:

$$2(Me_4N)_3Al(SO_3)_3 + 3SOCl_2 \rightarrow Al_2(SO_3)_3\downarrow + 6Me_4NCl + 6SO_2$$

Excess of thionyl chloride does not redissolve the aluminium sulphite, however, a deviation from the analogy with aqueous solutions.

Similar reactions are observed with gallium trichloride. When tetramethylammonium sulphite is added to a solution of gallium trichloride a precipitate is formed:

$$2GaCl_3 + 3(Me_4N)_2SO_3 \rightarrow 6Me_4NCl + Ga_2(SO_3)_3\downarrow$$

When excess of the sulphite is added, the precipitate redissolves. Again, stannic chloride solutions behave similarly; sulphite precipitates stannic sulphite, and this dissolves in excess of sulphite to give a solution of orthosulphitostannate, $(Me_4N)_4Sn(SO_3)_4$. A solution of PCl_3 in liquid sulphur dioxide, which is itself stable, gives, when a solution of tetramethylammonium sulphite is added, a flocculent precipitate of phosphorus trioxide:

$$2PCl_3 + 3(Me_4N)_2SO_3 \rightarrow P_2O_3 + 3SO_2 + 6Me_4NCl$$

On addition of further sulphite the precipitate redissolves, and from this solution the compound $Me_4NPO_2SO_2$ has been isolated:

$$P_2O_3 + (Me_4N)_2SO_3 + SO_2 \rightarrow 2(Me_4N)PO_2SO_2$$

This reaction has been followed conductimetrically and two end-points have been observed, the first at three moles of sulphite to two of PCl_3 and the second at four to two (see Fig. 3-2).

Metals which have amphoteric hydroxides generally dissolve in aqueous alkali with the liberation of hydrogen. Most of these, including beryllium, aluminium, gallium, antimony, and lead, give no reaction with tetramethylammonium sulphite in liquid sulphur

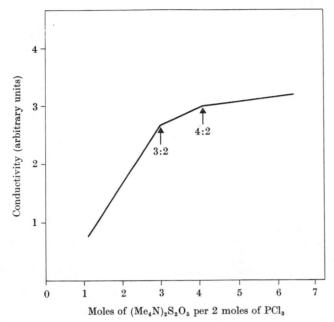

Fig. 3-2 Conductimetric titration of sulphite against PCl₃.

dioxide. However, tin does react. With excess of tetramethyl-ammonium sulphite the following reaction takes place:

$$Sn + 2(Me_4N)_2SO_3 + 3SO_2 \rightarrow (Me_4N)_2Sn(SO_3)_3 + (Me_4N)_2S_2O_3$$

the sulphur dioxide being reduced to thiosulphate.

Complex formation. Added iodine increases the conductivity of potassium iodide and rubidium iodide in liquid SO_2, and the solubility of iodine itself is greatly increased by the addition of potassium iodide or rubidium iodide. These effects are a maximum at an iodine:iodide ratio of 1:1 and are due to the formation of tri-iodide ion:

$$KI + I_2 \rightarrow KI_3$$

Similarly the solubilities of cadium iodide and mercuric iodide are increased by the addition of potassium iodide and rubidium iodide to the solvent, owing to the formation of complex ions:

$$HgI_2 + 2KI \rightarrow K_2HgI_4$$

Addition of $SbCl_3$ to a solution of KCl gives a precipitate of K_3SbCl_6:

$$3KCl + SbCl_3 \rightarrow K_3SbCl_6\!\downarrow$$

Addition of excess of antimony pentachloride causes this complex to dissolve with decomposition of the complex ion and formation of a hexachloroantimonate:

$$K_3SbCl_6 + 3SbCl_5 \rightarrow 3KSbCl_6 + SbCl_3$$

The preparation of a number of hexachloroantimonates in liquid SO_2 has been followed conductimetrically. When NOCl, $CH_3 \cdot COCl$, and $C_6H_5 \cdot COCl$ are titrated against $SbCl_5$ in SO_2, the conductimetric titrations show a sharp break at a ratio of 1:1, and the compounds NO^+SbCl_6, $CH_3 \cdot CO^+SbCl_6^-$ and $C_6H_5 \cdot CO^+SbCl_6^-$ can be isolated. The molar conductivities of these solutions are given in Table 3-10.

Table 3-10   The molar conductivities of $SbCl_5$ complexes in SO_2

Complex	Molar conductivity ($cm^2\ ohm^{-1}\ mol^{-1}$)
$KSbCl_6$	92·8
$(CH_3 \cdot CO)SbCl_6$	80·5
$(C_6H_5 \cdot CO)SbCl_6$	71·5
$(NO)SbCl_6$	67·5
$SOCl_2 + 2SbCl_5$	0·4

The data on the mixed solution of $SOCl_2$ and $SbCl_5$ are of interest. Early workers formulated this as $SO^{2+}(SbCl_6^-)_2$. The conductivity data show that there is no justification for this or for a formulation $(SOCl^+)(SbCl_6^-)$. The only solid adduct formed by $SOCl_2$ and $SbCl_5$ is $SOCl_2,SbCl_5$. No structural data are available for this compound, but X-ray diffraction studies have shown that the analogous compound $SeOCl_2,SbCl_5$ has an Se—O—Sb bond, being:

Cl
  \
    Se—O $\rightarrow$ SbCl$_5$
  /
Cl

It seems very likely that the thionyl chloride complex will have the same structure.

Oxidation–reduction reactions. In many oxidation–reduction reactions studied in SO_2, the solvent acts merely as an inert carrier. Tetramethylammonium sulphite is rapidly oxidized to the sulphate by iodine. A solution of ferric chloride will quantitatively oxidize KI to iodine:

$$2FeCl_3 + 2KI \rightarrow 2FeCl_2 + 2KCl + I_2$$

and so will a solution of antimony pentachloride:

$$6KI + 3SbCl_5 \rightarrow 3I_2 + 6KCl + 3SbCl_3$$

The reaction is complicated by the reaction of $SbCl_3$ with KCl and then the further reaction of excess of $SbCl_5$ with the precipitated K_3SbCl_6. In a conductimetric titration, in addition to a break at a mole ratio of $SbCl_5$ to KI of $1:2$, there is a break at a mole ratio of $3:2$ corresponding to:

$$2KI + 3SbCl_5 \rightarrow I_2 + 2KSbCl_6 + SbCl_3.$$

Nitrosyl compounds can act as oxidizing agents in liquid SO_2. Thus, with tetramethylammonium iodide:

$$2NOX + 2I^- \rightarrow 2NO + I_2 + 2X^- \qquad (X^- = Cl^- \text{ or } BF_4^-)$$

Ethyl nitrite acts in a similar manner:

$$2C_2H_5{\cdot}O{\cdot}NO + 2SO_2 + 2I^- \rightarrow 2NO + I_2 + 2SO_2{\cdot}OC_2H_5^-$$

With azides the reactions are:

$$NOX + N_3^- \rightarrow N_2O + N_2 + X^- \qquad (X^- = Cl^- \text{ or } BF_4^-)$$

and

$$C_2H_5{\cdot}O{\cdot}NO + N_3^- + SO_2 \rightarrow N_2O + N_2 + SO_2{\cdot}OC_2H_5^-$$

Reactions of organic compounds. Because many organic compounds are very soluble in liquid SO_2 and because it is itself inert to many of them, a range of synthetic organic reactions has been carried out in this solvent. These include sulphonations by sulphur trioxide or by chlorosulphuric acid:

$$C_6H_6 + SO_3 \rightarrow C_6H_5{\cdot}SO_3H$$
$$C_6H_6 + HSO_3Cl \rightarrow C_6H_5{\cdot}SO_3H + HCl$$

Sulphur dioxide has also been used as a solvent for Friedel–Crafts reactions because of the high solubility of aluminium chloride in it:

$$C_6H_6 + (CH_3)_3CCl \xrightarrow[SO_2]{AlCl_3} C_6H_5{\cdot}C(CH_3)_3 + HCl$$

$$C_6H_6 + C_6H_5{\cdot}C\underset{Cl}{\overset{\displaystyle O}{\diagup\!\!\!\diagdown}} \xrightarrow[SO_2]{AlCl_3} (C_6H_5)_2CO + HCl$$

It has also been used as a solvent for the addition of bromine to unsaturated compounds:

$$C_6H_5 \cdot CH:CH_2 + Br_2 \rightarrow C_6H_5 \cdot CHBr \cdot CH_2Br$$

3-2-3   Isotopic exchange studies and the proposed self-ionization of liquid sulphur dioxide

Early workers proposed a self-ionization equilibrium for liquid SO_2:

$$2SO_2 \rightarrow SO^{2+} + SO_3^{2-}$$

analogous to the self-ionization reactions of water and liquid ammonia, and suggested that sulphites would act as bases and thionyl compounds, such as $SOCl_2$ and $SOBr_2$, as acids in the solvent. The lack of evidence from conductivity data for SO^{2+}, or even $SOCl^+$ ions, has already been pointed out, but the strongest evidence against the proposed self-ionization comes from isotopic exchange studies in the solvent, mainly carried out by Norris and co-workers.

Neither $SOCl_2$ nor $SOBr_2$ exchange radioactively labelled sulphur, ^{35}S, or [18]O with solvent SO_2, but pyrosulphite ion, $S_2O_5^{2-}$ (sulphite dissolved in SO_2 can only be recovered as pyrosulphite), does give rapid ^{35}S exchange. Presumably [18]O exchange also takes place rapidly, though the measurements in this case have not been made. The thionyl halides, if ionizing at all, are only ionizing as:

$$SOX_2 = SOX^+ + X^-$$

and the low conductivity of their solutions in SO_2 indicates that this equilibrium, even in the presence of strong halide ion acceptors such as $SbCl_5$, must lie well to the left. Radioactive chlorine, [36]Cl, exchange does take rapidly between thionyl chloride and chloride ions in the solvent, but this may occur as a result of a simple associative equilibrium:

$$SOCl_2 + Cl^- = SOCl_3^-$$

The exchange of [18]O between sulphur dioxide and dissolved sulphur trioxide and the non-exchange of ^{35}S under the same conditions can be explained either by:

$$SO_2 + SO_3 = SO^{2+} + SO_4^{2-}$$

or by the formation of a transition complex such as:

which maintains the non-equivalence of the sulphur atoms. Since, however, sulphur trioxide solutions in liquid SO_2 have only the same low molar conductivities as solutions of $SOCl_2$, about $0 \cdot 1$ cm^2 ohm^{-1} mol^{-1}, the transition complex mechanism is favoured. This is confirmed by recent work which shows that homogeneous exchange of ^{18}O takes place in the gas between $S^{16}O_2$ and $S^{18}O_2$ mixtures. This can only take place through an intermediate such as:

$$O=S \overset{\displaystyle O}{\underset{\displaystyle O}{\diamondsuit}} S=O$$

It is unnecessary to postulate the involvement of the solvent to explain the metathetical reactions such as:

$$(Me_4N)_2SO_3 + SOCl_2 \rightarrow 2Me_4NCl + 2SO_2$$

This reaction could presumably occur in any inert solvent and does not require SO^{2+} or $SOCl^+$ as an intermediate. The reaction probably proceeds by nucleophilic attack of $S_2O_5^{2-}$ or SO_3^{2-} on $SOCl_2$, with expulsion of two chloride ions:

$$SO_3^{2-} + SOCl_2 = (SO_3 \cdot SOCl_2)^{2-} \rightarrow (SO_3 \cdot SOCl)^- + Cl^- \rightarrow$$
$$(SO_3 \cdot SO) + 2Cl^- \rightarrow 2SO_2 + 2Cl^-$$

Provided that the reaction is fast and the equilibrium:

$$SO_3^{2-} + SOCl_2 \rightleftharpoons 2SO_2 + 2Cl^-$$

is well over to the right then a conductimetric titration will show a break at a $1:1$ ratio of SO_3^{2-} to $SOCl_2$. It thus seems likely that SO_2 is not a self-ionizing solvent at all.

What does have to be explained is the remarkably good solvent and ionizing powers of liquid sulphur dioxide. Many ionic salts of fairly high lattice energy are much more soluble in liquid sulphur dioxide than its fairly low dielectric constant ($15 \cdot 3$) would lead one to expect. It also appears to have an unusual ionizing power. Triphenylchloromethane, which is covalent in the solid and in many common solvents, is extensively dissociated to Ph_3C^+ and Cl^- ions in liquid SO_2. Thus, in nitrobenzene (dielectric constant $34 \cdot 5$) it is too weak an electrolyte for a dissociation constant to be found while in SO_2 it is comparable as an electrolyte with tetramethylammonium chloride. Comparison of both dielectric constants and dipole moments, nitrobenzene ($\mu = 4 \cdot 24$, $D = 34 \cdot 8$) and SO_2 ($\mu = 1 \cdot 62$, $D = 15 \cdot 3$), indicates that some specific interaction must be sought for. There is a good deal of evidence that in SO_2 there is a specific charge-transfer interaction between the solvent and halide ions and it has been calculated that this complexing reduces the free energy of ionization of triphenylchloromethane by as much as 10 kcal mol^{-1}. The free energies of solution of ionic halides are affected in the same manner and this will have a profound effect on solubilities.

Problems

3-1   Comment critically on Jander's proposed ionization mechanism for liquid sulphur dioxide,

$$3SO_2 \rightleftharpoons SO^{2+} + S_2O_5^{2-}$$

in the light of your discussion of the following observations:

(i) *Pure* liquid SO_2 has a very low conductivity.

(ii) Tetramethylammonium sulphite dissolves readily in liquid SO_2 and enhances the conductivity.

(iii) The electrical conductivity of liquid SO_2 increases when sulphur trioxide is dissolved in it; addition of a soluble sulphite to the resultant solution decreases the conductivity.

(iv) There is rapid ^{18}O exchange between $S^{18}O_3$ and liquid SO_2 when labelled sulphur trioxide is dissolved in the solvent. There is no radio-active sulphur exchange when *SO_3 is dissolved in SO_2.

(v) Thionyl chloride containing radiosulphur dissolved in liquid SO_2 enhances the conductivity, but none of the radioactive sulphur is transferred to the solvent molecules.

(vi) Aluminium chloride in liquid sulphur dioxide reacts with sodium sulphite to give a precipitate which dissolves when excess of sulphite is added. What would you expect to happen when thionyl chloride labelled with ^{18}O is dissolved in liquid sulphur dioxide?

3-2   Give an account of the use of liquid N_2O_4 as a solvent in preparative inorganic chemistry.

Bibliography

1. ADDISON, C. C.   Use of non-aqueous solvents in inorganic chemistry. *R. Inst. Chem. Lecture Series*, 1960 (2).

2. ADDISON, C. C. and B. J. HATHAWAY.   Addition compounds of dinitrogen tetroxide and their applications in preparative inorganic chemistry, in *Recent aspects of inorganic chemistry*, Special Publication No. 10. Chemical Society, London, 1957.

3. GRAY, P. and A. D. YOFFE.   Structure and reactivity of the nitrogen dioxide–dinitrogen tetroxide system. *Q. Rev. chem. Soc.*, 1955, **9**, 362.

4. JANDER, G.   Die Chemie in verflüssigtem Schwefeldioxyd. Chapter 3 in *Die Chemie in Wasserahnlichen Losungsmitteln*, Springer Verlag, Heidelberg, 1949.

5. WADDINGTON, T. C.   Liquid sulphur dioxide. Chapter 6 in *Non-aqueous solvent systems*, edited by T. C. WADDINGTON. Academic Press, London and New York, 1965.

Oxyhalide solvents

In this chapter the oxyhalides NOCl and $POCl_3$ will be considered as solvents. Apart from the many useful preparations that can be carried out in them, their chief interest lies in their mode of action. Do they function simply as coordinating solvents, acting as electron pair donors through the oxygen, or possibly as weak acceptors through the nitrogen or the phosphorus? Is solvent self-ionization an important reaction in these solvents, and are reactions like:

$$NOCl \rightleftharpoons NO^+ + Cl^-$$

of importance?

4-1 Nitrosyl chloride

Some of the more important physical properties of nitrosyl chloride are listed in Table 4-1. On the basis of its reasonably high dielectric

Table 4-1 Physical properties of nitrosyl chloride

Melting point (°C)	$-64 \cdot 5$
Boiling point (°C)	$-5 \cdot 5$
Liquid range (°C)	59
Viscosity (centipoise)	$0 \cdot 586$ (-27°C)
Density (g cm^{-3})	$1 \cdot 59$ (-6°C)
Dielectric constant	$19 \cdot 7$ (-10°C); $22 \cdot 5$ (-27°C)
Specific conductivity (ohm^{-1} cm^{-1})	$2 \cdot 88 \times 10^{-6}$ (-20°C)
Dipole moment (Debye)	$1 \cdot 83$

constant nitrosyl chloride would be expected to be a fairly good ionizing solvent. However, materials such as potassium chloride are insoluble in the solvent and it is necessary to go to the tetra-alkyl-ammonium halides to achieve solubility. Nitrosyl chloride has, however, remarkable solvent properties for nitrosonium salts. Since these salts will have very similar lattice energies to the corresponding potassium and rubidium salts (the crystal radius of the nitrosonium ion, NO^+, is estimated to be $1 \cdot 45$ Å) there must be a fairly specific solvation interaction. Since both $(NO)AlCl_4$ and $(NO)FeCl_4$ form solid adducts $(NO)AlCl_4,NOCl$ and $(NO)FeCl_4,NOCl$ it is believed that this interaction is the formation of a species such as:

$$[O{=}N{-}Cl{-}N{=}O]^+$$

Compounds such as $(NO)AlCl_4$, $(NO)FeCl_4$, and $(NO)SbCl_6$ are readily soluble and are strong electrolytes. However the $2:1$ electrolytes $(NO)_2SnCl_6$ and $(NO)_2TiCl_6$ are not soluble. Some typical values of conductivities in nitrosyl chloride are given in Table 4-2.

Table 4-2   Conductivities of some nitrosonium salts in NOCl

Salt	Molarity	Temperature ($^{\circ}C$)	Specific conductivity (ohm^{-1} cm^{-1})	Molar conductivity cm^2 ohm^{-1} mol^{-1}
$NO(AlCl_4)$	0·098	-20	$1·17 \times 10^{-2}$	119
$NO(FeCl_4)$	0·0099	-20	$1·34 \times 10^{-3}$	136
$NO(FeCl_4)$	0·0094	-44	$1·00 \times 10^{-3}$	106
$NO(SbCl_6)$	0·140	-20	$2·35 \times 10^{-2}$	168
$NO(SbCl_6)$	0·140	-44	$2·20 \times 10^{-2}$	157

The molar conductivities quoted are, of course, not limiting molar conductivities, but are probably not too far from the limiting values. It can be seen that, though smaller, they are of the same order of magnitude as molar conductivities in water. The molar conductivity of $(NO)FeCl_4$ in nitrosyl chloride has been studied as a function of concentration at $-10^{\circ}C$ and fitted to the Shedlovsky equation. This leads to a value of $401·2$ cm^2 ohm^{-1} mol^{-1} for Λ_0, the limiting molar conductivity of $NO(FeCl_4)$. The transport number of the nitrosonium ion was found to be $0·88$ in these solutions leading to a λ_0, limiting mobility, value for NO^+ of 353 cm^2 ohm^{-1} g-ion^{-1} and a λ_0 value for $FeCl_4^-$ of 48 cm^2 ohm^{-1} g-ion^{-1}. This anomalously high value for the mobility of the NO^+ ion suggests very strongly that a Grotthus chain mechanism, analogous to the transport of the H^+ ion in water, must be occurring. The above conclusion is also supported by the fact that the specific conductivity of $Me_4N^+FeCl_4^-$ is about $0·28$ that of $(NO)FeCl_4$ at the same concentration, implying that the limiting mobility of the Me_4N^+ ion will be about 64 cm^2 ohm^{-1} g-ion^{-1} at $-10^{\circ}C$. Unfortunately we have no value for the mobility of the chloride ion in the solvent. This sort of evidence does seem to support the importance of the ionization:

$$NOCl \rightleftharpoons NO^+ + Cl^-$$

in the solvent.

Conductimetric titrations can also be carried out in the solvent and Fig. 4-1 shows the results of such a titration between $(NO)FeCl_4$ and Me_4NCl.

Isotopic studies using radioactive chlorine, ^{36}Cl, have shown that rapid exchange of chlorine takes place between $AlCl_3$, $GaCl_3$, $InCl_3$,

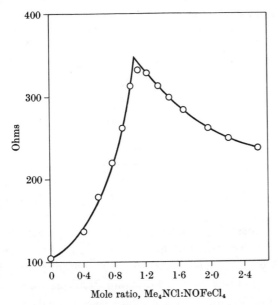

Fig. 4-1 Conductimetric titration of (NO)FeCl₄ with
Me₄NCl in NOCl at −10°C.

TeCl₃, FeCl₃, and SbCl₅ and the solvent. All chlorine atoms in these
materials appear to be equivalent. Some exchange of ³⁶Cl between
ZnCl₂, CdCl₂, and HgCl₂, which are not significantly soluble, and
nitrosyl chloride also takes place fairly rapidly. This is presumed to
take place as a result of the formation of the 1:1 complex, which is
insoluble. This is followed by a slower heterogeneous exchange of
chlorine between the complex and the solvent. No exchange was
found with sodium chloride and potassium chloride and the solvent.
This must be due to their insolubility.

Not many studies of chemical reactions in the solvent have been
made, but the reactions of the silver phosphates are worthy of note:

$$4Ag_3PO_4 + 12NOCl \rightarrow (NO)_2P_4O_{11} + 5N_2O_3 + 12AgCl$$
$$3Ag_4P_2O_7 + 12NOCl \rightarrow (NO)_4P_6O_{17} + 4N_2O_3 + 12AgCl$$
$$Ag_3P_3O_9 + 3NOCl \rightarrow (NO)P_3O_8 + N_2O_3 + 3AgCl$$
$$Ag_4P_4O_{12} + 4NOCl \rightarrow (NO)_2P_4O_{11} + N_2O_3 + 4AgCl$$

The reactions produce additional P—O—P bond formation, rather
surprisingly in the case of the silver tri- and tetra-metaphosphates.

4-2 Phosphoryl chloride

Some important physical properties of phosphoryl chloride are listed
in Table 4-3. It is worth noting the comparatively long liquid range
of POCl₃ and its much higher viscosity than NOCl, in spite of its

Table 4-3   Physical properties of phosphoryl chloride

Melting point (°C)	1
Boiling point (°C)	108
Liquid range (°C)	107
Viscosity (centipoise)	1·15 (25°C)
Density (g cm^{-3})	1·71 (0°)
Dielectric constant	13·9 (22°C)
Specific conductivity (ohm^{-1} cm^{-1})	<2 × 10^{-8}
Trouton's constant	24·9
Enthalpy of vaporization (kcal mol^{-1})	9·5

lower dielectric constant. This suggests that it is probably more associated than NOCl.

In general the solubilities of the alkali halides in phosphoryl chloride are low, but are a great deal higher than in nitrosyl chloride, again in spite of the lower dielectric constant. The alkaline earth halides, silver chloride, mercurous chloride, and thallous chloride are insoluble. Some solubilities and conductivities are given in Table 4-4.

Quaternary ammonium salts are very soluble. Compounds such as $SiCl_4$, $SiBr_4$, and $SnBr_4$ dissolve readily and are molecular in the solvent. PCl_5, $AsCl_3$, $BiCl_3$, ICl_3, SCl_4, $PtCl_4$, PBr_5, $BiBr_3$, and BiI_3 are readily soluble, but cryoscopic measurements indicate that they are dissociated. BCl_3, $AlCl_3$, $SbCl_5$, $SnCl_4$, $TiCl_4$, $TeCl_4$, and BBr_3 all are readily soluble but form adducts with the solvent. A list of $POCl_3$ adducts is given in Table 4-5.

The dielectric constant of $POCl_3$ is sufficiently low for soluble ionic compounds to show a molar conductivity minimum in the solvent,

Table 4-4   Solubilities and conductivities of some simple salts in POCl$_3$

Salt	Solubility (g l^{-1})	Specific conductivity (ohm^{-1} cm^{-1}) × 10^5	Molar conductivity of 10^{-3} M solution (cm^2 ohm^{-1} mol^{-1})
LiCl	0·05	0·66	4·0
NaCl	0·31	3·0	6·4
KCl	~0·60	3·4	6·7
NH$_4$Cl	0·46	3·6	6·9
RbCl	0·87	8·3	14·6
CsCl	1·26	11·0	16·0
KF	~0·40	2·6	6·4
KBr	0·51	4·3	14·5
KI	~1·71	12·0	23·1
KCN	~0·73	3·3	7·2
KNCO	~0·80	3·1	9·0
KNCS	~0·76	2·9	6·6

Table 4-5   Adducts formed between Lewis acids and $POCl_3$

Lewis acid	Adduct	Structure
$SbCl_5$	$SbCl_5,POCl_3$	$Cl_3PO \rightarrow SbCl_5$
$GaCl_3$	$GaCl_3,POCl_3$	$Cl_3PO \rightarrow GaCl_3$
$GaCl_3$	$GaCl_3,2POCl_3$	
BCl_3	$BCl_3,POCl_3$	$Cl_3PO \rightarrow BCl_3$
$AlCl_3$	$AlCl_3,POCl_3$	$Cl_3PO \rightarrow AlCl_3$
$AlCl_3$	$AlCl_3,2POCl_3$	
$AlCl_3$	$AlCl_3,6POCl_3$	$Al(OPCl_3)_6^{3+}(Cl^-)_3$ (?)
$GaBr_3$	$GaBr_3,POCl_3$	
$SnCl_4$	$SnCl_4,POCl_3$	$Cl_3PO \rightarrow SnCl_4$
$SnCl_4$	$SnCl_4,2POCl_3$	
$FeCl_3$	$FeCl_3,POCl_3$	$Cl_3PO \rightarrow FeCl_3$
$FeCl_3$	$2FeCl_3,POCl_3$	
$FeCl_3$	$2FeCl_3,3POCl_3$	$FeCl(OPCl_3)_3^+ FeCl_4^-$ (?)

Lewis acid	Adduct	Structure
$TiCl_4$	$2TiCl_4,2POCl_3$	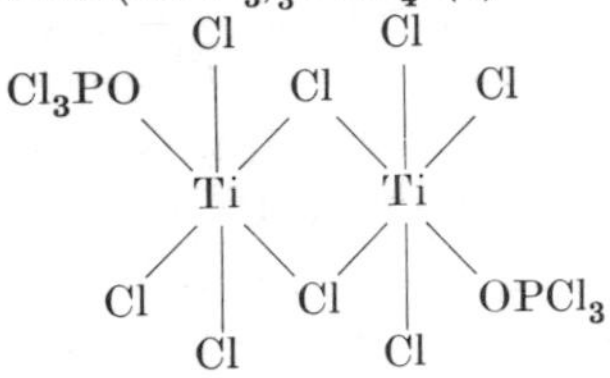

$$Cl_3PO \diagdown$$
$$TiCl_4$$
$$Cl_3PO \diagup$$

| $TiCl_4$ | $TiCl_4,2POCl_3$ | 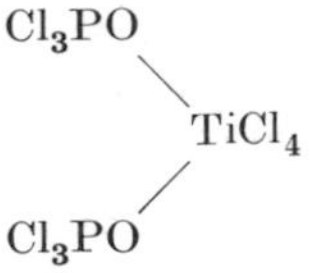 |

just as in SO_2. However, at concentrations below about 5×10^{-3} M, triple ions are in negligible concentration and the data can be interpreted in terms of an ion pair–free ion equilibrium,

$$[M^+X^-] \rightleftharpoons M^+ + X^-$$

and hence ion pair dissociation constants and limiting values of equivalent conductivity found. Table 4-6 gives some data for such systems.

Table 4-6   Values of the limiting equivalent conductivities, Λ_0, for some quarternary ammonium salts in $POCl_3$

Salt	Λ_0 (cm² ohm⁻¹ mol⁻¹)
Et_4NCl	53·0
Pr_4NCl	47·6
Bu_4NCl	44·4
Et_4NBr	50·0
Et_4NI	48·5
Et_4NClO_4	53·4
$Et_3N \cdot POCl_2^+Cl^-$	48·5

The values of limiting equivalent conductivity are rather low when compared with other solvents, perhaps owing to the viscosity of the solvent. They also indicate clearly that the mobility of the chloride ion is not anomalous. This is important in relation to the proposed self-ionization of the solvent:

$$POCl_3 \rightleftharpoons POCl_2^+ \text{ (solvated)} + Cl^- \text{ (solvated)}$$

Even if this is of importance, a Grotthus mechanism involving the chloride ion is ruled out.

Triethylamine dissolves in phosphoryl chloride to give a conducting solution. The behaviour can be represented by the equilibrium:

$$(C_2H_5)_3N + POCl_3 \rightleftharpoons [(C_2H_5)_3N \cdot POCl_2^+Cl^-] \rightleftharpoons (C_2H_5)_3N \cdot POCl_2^+ + Cl^-$$

and from the variation of conductivity with dilution a value of Λ_0 of $48 \cdot 5$ cm^2 ohm^{-1} mol^{-1} can be obtained.

In spite of the fact that all the solid adducts of $POCl_3$ with Lewis acids which have been investigated contain an oxygen link to the Lewis acid from the $POCl_3$, solutions of many Lewis acids in $POCl_3$ are conducting. This was originally interpreted in terms of the equilibria:

$$POCl_3 + SbCl_5 \rightarrow POCl_2^+ + SbCl_6^-$$
$$POCl_3 + AlCl_3 \rightarrow POCl_2^+ + AlCl_4^-$$
$$POCl_3 + FeCl_3 \rightarrow POCl_2^+ + FeCl_4^-$$

but it is equally possible to interpret the conductivities in terms of equilibria such as:

$$2POCl_3 + AlCl_3 \rightarrow (Cl_3PO)_2AlCl_2^+ + Cl^-$$
$$5POCl_3 + AlCl_3 \rightarrow (Cl_3PO)_5AlCl^{2+} + 2Cl^-$$

and

$$6POCl_3 + AlCl_3 \rightarrow (Cl_3PO)_6Al^{3+} + 3Cl^-$$

A comparison of the behaviour of $FeCl_3$ in $POCl_3$ and in triethylphosphate, $PO(OC_2H_5)_3$, has confirmed the existence of equilibria of the above type. Absorption bands characteristic of $FeCl_4^-$ are observed in both solvents. Use of triethylphosphate as a solvent excludes the possibility of the tetrachloroferrate ion being formed from a chloride ion liberated by self-ionization of the solvent. The following set of equilibria occur:

$$FeCl_3 + Y_3PO \rightleftharpoons (FeCl_3OPY_3) \rightleftharpoons FeCl_{3-x}(OPY_3)_{1+x}^{x+} + xFeCl_4^-$$

The molar conductivities of some solutions of aluminium halides are given in Table 4-7. These values are a good deal lower than the

Table 4-7 Molar conductivities of aluminium halides in $POCl_3$ (cm^2 ohm^{-1} mol^{-1})

	0·05 M	0·1 M	0·2 M
AlF_3	0·088		
$AlCl_3$	7·2	7·7	7·6
$AlBr_3$	9·0	9·1	9·1
AlI_3	8·0	8·1	8·1

limiting conductivities of the tetra-alkylammonium salts, but they are probably measured at concentrations near the conductivity minimum.

4-2-1 Chemical reactions in phosphoryl chloride

Straightforward conductimetric titrations between tetramethyl-ammonium chloride and both ferric chloride and antimony trichloride can be performed and give sharp 1:1 end-points:

$$Me_4NCl + FeCl_3 \rightarrow Me_4NFeCl_4$$
$$Me_4NCl + SbCl_3 \rightarrow Me_4NSbCl_4$$

However, similar titrations can also be carried out in triethyl phosphate. Whatever the species present in solution, as long as the equilibria in the following equations lie well over to the right, these sharp 1:1 end-points are to be expected:

$$FeCl_2(OPY_3)_4^+ + 2Cl^- \rightarrow FeCl_4^-$$
$$FeCl(OPY_3)_5^{2+} + 3Cl^- \rightarrow FeCl_4^-$$
$$Fe(OPY_3)_6^{3+} + 4Cl^- \rightarrow FeCl_4^-$$
$$FeCl_3(OPY_3) + Cl^- \rightarrow FeCl_4^-$$

Since the iron:chlorine ratio in a solution of $FeCl_3$ is 1:3, only one mole of chloride ion per mole of $FeCl_3$ will be required to convert all the iron to $FeCl_4^-$.

Just as triethylamine gives conducting solutions in $POCl_3$, so does pyridine and it would appear that the mechanism is similar:

$$C_5H_5N + POCl_3 \rightarrow C_5H_5N \cdot POCl_2^+ + Cl^-$$

These solutions can be titrated with VCl_4, PCl_5, and $TaCl_5$ solutions and such titrations show breaks at 1:2, 1:1, and 1:1 mole ratios of pyridine to Lewis acid respectively, corresponding to the reactions:

$$2C_5H_5N \cdot POCl_2^+ + 2Cl^- + VCl_4 \rightarrow (C_5H_5N \cdot POCl_2^+)_2VCl_6^{2-}$$
$$C_5H_5N \cdot POCl_2^+ + Cl^- + PCl_5 \rightarrow (C_5H_5N \cdot POCl_2^+)PCl_6^-$$

and

$$C_5H_5N \cdot POCl_2^+ + Cl^- + TaCl_5 \rightarrow (C_5H_5N \cdot POCl_2^+)TaCl_6^-$$

The compounds do not appear to have been isolated, however.

A number of solutions containing two different Lewis acid chlorides have been studied. Unfortunately the results of conductimetric titrations do not always seem to be unambiguous, chiefly owing to the formation of colloidal micelles and precipitates during the addition of the solution of one chloride to another. However, the compounds $2AlCl_3,SnCl_4,2POCl_3$, and $AlCl_3,SbCl_5,3POCl_3$ have been isolated as precipitates from the addition of $SnCl_4$ and $SbCl_5$ solutions respectively to solutions of $AlCl_3$.

With solutions of $TiCl_4$ in $POCl_3$, addition of $SbCl_5$ leads to the isolation of a solid of composition $TiCl_4,SbCl_5,3POCl_3$ which has been shown by X-ray studies to have the structure $TiCl_3(OPCl_3)_3^+SbCl_6^-$. Addition of KCl to a solution of $TiCl_4$ leads to the isolation of a solid $K^+TiCl_5(OPCl_3)^-$.

Some preliminary results on the reactions of silver salts with the solvent, $POCl_3$, are worth recording. Addition of silver borofluoride leads to the precipitation of AgCl, but not to the isolation of a $POCl_2^+$ salt. Instead it appears that probably $POCl_2F$ and BF_3 are produced. Silver salts in general, such as silver nitrate, will precipitate silver chloride from the solvent, but do not appear to give $POCl_2^+$ salts.

4-2-2 Conclusion

Though there may very well be a solvent auto-ionization:

$$POCl_3 \rightleftharpoons POCl_2^+ \text{ (solvated)} + Cl^- \text{ (solvated)}$$

and though the concentration of chloride ions can be increased by the addition of triethylamine or pyridine, no method of increasing the concentration of $POCl_2^+$ ions in the solution has been devised. Assigning a realistic value to the limiting equivalent conductivity of $[POCl_2^+][Cl^-]$ of 50 cm² ohm⁻¹ mol⁻¹ leads to a concentration of $POCl_2^+$ ions in the pure liquid of 4×10^{-7} g-ions l⁻¹, and this must be regarded as an upper limit. Addition of Lewis acid chlorides appears to lead either to production of neutral adducts bonded through the oxygen of the $POCl_3$ or to the production of ionic species by displacement of chloride ions from the Lewis acid chlorides by $POCl_3$ molecules, as in the case of aluminium chloride and ferric chloride.

In spite of its lower dielectric constant, $POCl_3$ is a better solvent than NOCl, and this is probably due to the ability of the $POCl_3$ molecule to coordinate with cations, particularly with transition metal cations, by donation of an electron pair from its oxygen atom.

It probably also coordinates weakly with halide anions, such as chloride ion, by the phosphorus atom accepting an electron pair from the halide ion. Neither of these mechanisms seems to operate as strongly with nitrosyl chloride.

Problems

4-1 Discuss the techniques available for the identification of the species present in solutions of inorganic solutes in non-aqueous ionizing solvents. $FeCl_3$ gives a conducting solution in $POCl_3$. Tracer experiments show that the chlorine atoms in the two compounds only exchange quite slowly, but that exchange is greatly accelerated by the addition of tetramethylammonium chloride. Suggest interpretations of these observations, and describe methods for distinguishing between the various possibilities you propose.

4-2 Liquid NOCl has a low electrical conductivity, which is very much increased on addition of $AlCl_3$. The resulting solution attacks metals with evolution of NO. Discuss this.

Bibliography

1. GUTMAN, V. Covalent oxyhalides as solvents, in *Halogen chemistry*, *Vol. 2*, edited by V. GUTMANN. Academic Press, London and New York, 1967.
2. PAYNE, D. S. Halides and oxyhalides of Group V elements as solvents, in *Non-aqueous solvent systems*, edited by T. C. WADDINGTON. Academic Press, London and New York, 1965.

5 Liquid halides as ionizing solvents

In this chapter we are concerned with the behaviour of some halides, usually considered to be covalent, which function as ionizing solvents. They are AsF_3, $AsCl_3$, $AsBr_3$, and $SbCl_3$, and the interhalogen compounds ICl and BrF_3.

5-1 Arsenic trihalides

Of the arsenic trihalides only the trichloride has been studied in any detail, and even for this we have only a few physicochemical measurements. A comparison of physical properties is given in Table 5-1.

Table 5-1 Physical properties of the arsenic trihalides

	AsF_3	$AsCl_3$	$AsBr_3$
Melting point (°C)	−6	−13	35
Boiling point (°C)	63	130	220
Liquid range (°C)	69	143	185
Viscosity (centipoise)	8·57 (20°C)	1·225 (20°C)	5·41 (35°C)
			4·44 (48°C)
Density (g cm^{-3})	2·45 (20°C)	2·16 (20°C)	3·33 (50°C)
Dielectric constant	5·7 (−6°C)	12·6 (17°C)	8·8 (35°C)
Specific conductivity (ohm cm^{-1})	2·4 × 10^{-5}	1·4 × 10^{-7}	1·6 × 10^{-7}

5-1-1 Arsenic trichloride

As a solvent, the suggested self-ionization is:

$$2AsCl_3 \rightleftharpoons AsCl_2^+ + AsCl_4^-$$

and similar self-ionizations would probably also apply to the other trihalides. The dielectric constant is fairly small; consequently, the solubilities of the alkali metal chlorides and ammonium chloride are very low. However, the tetra-alkylammonium halides are readily soluble. $NbCl_5$ and $TaCl_5$ are not very soluble, but $AlCl_3$, $SnCl_4$, VCl_4, and $FeCl_3$ are very soluble. Various non-metals such as sulphur, phosphorus, and iodine also dissolve readily, but the nature of these solutions is unknown. Metals, metal oxides, and oxy-salts, such as sulphates and nitrates, are either insoluble or have very low solubilities. A wide range of solvates is formed by the solvent, mostly of halides. A list of these is given in Table 5-2, together with compounds isolated from aqueous solutions, containing hydrochloric acid and $AsCl_3$.

Table 5-2   Adducts of $AsCl_3$ and their formulation

Salt	Adduct	Formulation	How isolated
KCl	$KCl,AsCl_3$	$K^+AsCl_4^-$	(a) Aqueous solution
			(b) KCl in contact with liquid $AsCl_3$
RbCl	$3RbCl,2AsCl_3$	$Rb_3^+(As_2Cl_9^{3-})$	Aqueous solution
CsCl	$3CsCl,2AsCl_3$	$Cs_3^+(As_2Cl_9^{3-})$	Aqueous solution
$EtNH_3Cl$	$2EtNH_3Cl,AsCl_3$	$(EtNH_3^+)(AsCl_5^{2-})$	Aqueous solution
$MeNH_3Cl$	$3MeNH_3Cl,2AsCl_3$	$(MeNH_3^+)_3(As_2Cl_9^{3-})$	Aqueous solution
Me_2NH_2Cl	$Me_2NH_2Cl,AsCl_3$	$(Me_2NH_2^+)AsCl_4^-$	Aqueous solution
Me_3NHCl	$2Me_3NHCl,3AsCl_3$	$(Me_3NH^+)_2(As_3Cl_{11}^{2-})$	Aqueous solution
Me_4NCl	$Me_4NCl,3AsCl_3$		From $AsCl_3$
Me_4NCl	$Me_4NCl,AsCl_3$	$Me_4N^+AsCl_4^-$	From $AsCl_3$, high temperature
Et_4NCl	$Et_4NCl,2AsCl_3$	$Et_4N^+As_2Cl_7^-$	From $AsCl_3$
PCl_5	$PCl_5,AsCl_3$	$PCl_4^+AsCl_4^-$	From $AsCl_3$

Chemical reactions in arsenic trichloride. Solutions of both tetramethylammonium chloride and antimony pentachloride have high conductivities in $AsCl_3$. A conductimetric titration of these solutions shows a break at a $1:1$ end-point (Fig. 5-1).

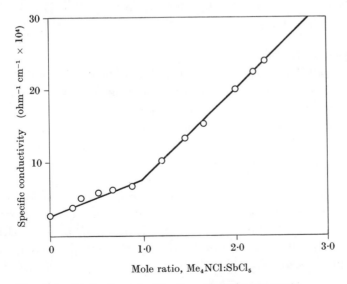

Fig. 5-1 Conductimetric titration of antimony pentachloride with tetramethylammonium chloride in arsenic trichloride.

The salt Me_4NSbCl_6 can be isolated from the solution. The reaction is probably:

$$Me_4N^+AsCl_4^- + AsCl_2^+SbCl_6^- = Me_4N^+SbCl_6^- + 2AsCl_3$$

since the antimony pentachloride solution has a high conductivity.

Tellurium tetrachloride dissolves in $AsCl_3$ to give a conducting solution which, in a conductimetric titration against Me_4NCl, gives end-points at an acid–base ratio of $1:1$ and $1:2$. From the $1:1$ solution a solid of composition $Me_4NCl,TeCl_4,AsCl_3$ can be isolated, which may be formulated as $Me_4N^+AsCl_2^+TeCl_6^{2-}$. From the $1:2$ solution, solid $(Me_4N^+)_2TeCl_6^{2-}$ can be obtained. When $TeCl_4$ is titrated with $SbCl_5$ in $AsCl_3$, breaks are found at molar ratios of $2:1$ and $1:1$ $TeCl_4$ to $SbCl_5$. From the $2:1$ solution a solid of composition $2TeCl_4,SbCl_5,AsCl_3$ has been isolated. This can be formulated as $(TeCl_3^+)_2AsCl_4^-SbCl_6^-$. From the $1:1$ solution a solid of composition $TeCl_4,SbCl_5$, which is probably $TeCl_3^+SbCl_6^-$, can be isolated.

Pyridine solutions in arsenic trichloride are good conductors of electricity and probably function by liberating chloride ion:

$$C_5H_5N + 2AsCl_3 \rightarrow C_5H_5N{\cdot}AsCl_2^+ + AsCl_4^-$$

Such solutions can be titrated against $SnCl_4$ and VCl_4. In both cases the conductimetric titration curves show a break at an end-point of $1:2$ and solids of composition $2C_5H_5N,2AsCl_3,SnCl_4$ and $2C_5H_5N,2AsCl_3,VCl_4$, which are presumably $(C_5H_5N{\cdot}AsCl_2^+)_2SnCl_6^{2-}$ and $(C_5H_5N{\cdot}AsCl_2^+)_2VCl_6^{2-}$.

5-1-2   Arsenic trifluoride

Arsenic trifluoride has a fairly high specific conductivity, but this may be due to impurities. In spite of its low dielectric constant, potassium fluoride dissolves readily in the solvent, as do rubidium fluoride and caesium fluoride. From these solutions the compounds $KAsF_4$, $RbAsF_4$, and $CsAsF_4$ can be isolated, and it is the formation of the complex ion, AsF_4^-, and of probably higher complexes in solution that explains the solubility of the fluorides.

Antimony pentafluoride also dissolves in the solvent to give a conducting solution, from which a compound of composition AsF_3,SbF_5, which can be formulated as $AsF_2^+SbF_6^-$, can be isolated.

Conductimetric titrations of solutions of potassium fluoride and antimony pentafluoride give a $1:1$ end-point and also produce solid $KSbF_6$:

$$AsF_2^+SbF_6^- + K^+AsF_4^- \rightarrow KSbF_6{\downarrow} + 2AsF_3$$

Chemical reactions in arsenic trifluoride. When chlorine is passed into AsF_3 at 0°C a white crystalline substance, $AsCl_4^+AsF_6^-$, is formed. Many chlorine-containing compounds react with the solvent. Thus $SbCl_5$ reacts as follows:

$$3SbCl_5 + AsF_3 \rightarrow 3SbCl_4^+F^- + AsCl_3$$

N.M.R. studies of arsenic trifluoride. [19]F studies of AsF_3 and of solutions of alkali metal fluorides show that the latter have only one resonance line, shifted slightly from that of AsF_3. This indicates that the solvated fluoride ion, or the AsF_4^- ion, exchanges fluorines sufficiently rapidly with AsF_3 to give only a single n.m.r. resonance. Similarly, the ^{19}F spectrum of an arsenic trifluoride–antimony pentafluoride mixture shows only one resonance peak, in a position between the resonances of the two pure compounds. This means that rapid exchange between AsF_3 and SbF_5 via fluorine bridges must occur:

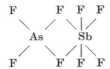

5-1-3 Arsenic tribromide

The alkali, alkaline earth, and divalent transition metal bromides and salts of oxy-acids and metal oxides do not appear to have an appreciable solubility. $HgBr_2$, $InBr_3$, $TeBr_4$, and $BiBr_3$ are all moderately soluble. Quaternary ammonium bromides and BBr_3, $AlBr_3$, $GaBr_3$, $SnBr_4$, $TiBr_4$, PBr_3, PBr_5, $SbBr_3$, and $SeBr_4$ are readily soluble. Many organic compounds, including aromatic hydrocarbons, alcohols, ketones, aldehydes, esters, and amines, are freely soluble in the solvent.

Solvates of the type $R_4NBr,AsBr_3$ are formed with quaternary ammonium bromides, and with other organic bases, B, solvates of the type $B,HBr,AsBr_3$ are found. Both types should probably be formulated as containing the $AsBr_4^-$ ion. Cryoscopic measurements show that with anhydro bases like triethylamine and pyridine an equilibrium occurs:

$$(C_2H_5)_3N + 2AsBr_3 \rightleftharpoons (C_2H_5)_3N \cdot AsBr_2^+ + AsBr_4^-$$

Addition of silver salts, such as silver perchlorate, at 50°C leads to the precipitation of AgBr and a solution of high conductivity;

$$AsBr_3 + AgClO_4 = AsBr_2^+ClO_4^- + AgBr\downarrow$$

It is, however, not possible to isolate $AsBr_2^+ClO_4^-$ as a solid compound.

The Lewis acids $AlBr_3$, $GaBr_3$, $InBr_3$, BBr_3, $SnBr_4$, $HgBr_2$, and $TeBr_4$ may be employed in conductimetric titration against tetra-alkylammonium bromide in the solution and a variety of salts may be isolated from this solution. The results of some titrations are shown in Fig. 5-2.

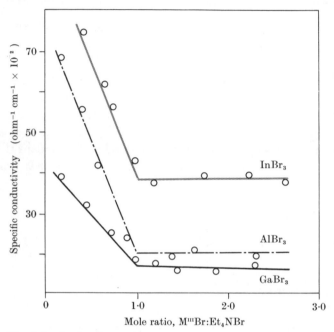

Fig. 5-2   Conductimetric titration of Et_4NBr with $InBr_3$, $AlBr_3$, and $GaBr_3$ in arsenic tribromide solutions.

5-1-4   Conclusion and comparison

There seems to be good evidence that self-ionization occurs in all three arsenic trihalides:

$$2AsX_3 \rightleftharpoons AsX_2^+ + AsX_4^-$$

and that concentrations of both species can be increased by addition of appropriate base or acid. In all cases solids of the type $MAsX_4$ can be isolated and in some cases solids containing the species AsX_2^+.

Unfortunately not enough conductivity data have yet been accumulated to say whether a Grotthus hopping mechanism occurs in the solvent and whether anomalously high mobilities are to be associated with the species AsX_2^+ and AsX_4^-. However, the results of [19]F n.m.r. studies on AsF_3 indicate that this may occur.

5-2   Antimony trichloride

Some of the physical properties of antimony trichloride are listed in Table 5-3.

Table 5-3　Physical properties of SbCl$_3$

Melting point (°C)	73
Boiling point (°C)	219–223
Liquid range (°C)	150
Viscosity (centipoise)	3·3(95°C)
Density (g cm^{-3})	2·44(178°C)
Dielectric constant	33·0 (75°C)
Specific conductivity (ohm^{-1} cm^{-1})	0·85 × 10^{-6} (95°C)
Trouton's constant	~21
Enthalpy of vaporization (kcal mol^{-1})	10–36
Molar cryoscopic constant (deg mol^{-1} kg)	15·6 ± 0·2

Unlike their behaviour in arsenic trichloride, KCl, RbCl, CsCl, and NH$_4$Cl are readily soluble in antimony trichloride, as are the quaternary ammonium chlorides. HgCl$_2$, AlCl$_3$, SbCl$_5$, and TeCl$_4$ are also readily soluble. However, LiCl, NaCl, SnCl$_2$, BiCl$_3$, and FeCl$_3$ have only at most a slight solubility. With the exception of their tetra-alkylammonium salts, sulphates and perchlorates are insoluble. Many organic compounds such as aromatic hydrocarbons, organic halides, and oxygen- and sulphur- containing compounds are soluble, and the solubility of proteins and nucleic acids in the solvent has been utilized in the study of their infrared O—H and N—H vibration frequencies. A wide variety of solvates with inorganic chlorides is formed; some of these are KSbCl$_4$, K$_2$SbCl$_5$, KSb$_2$Cl$_7$, K$_3$Sb$_2$Cl$_9$ Ba(SbCl$_4$)$_2$, and BaSbCl$_5$.

The limiting conductivities of a wide variety of chlorides and bromides have been determined and are listed in Table 5-4. The closeness of the values of these limiting conductivities suggests that both chloride and bromide ions have an anomalously high mobility in SbCl$_3$. This is confirmed by an experimental value of 0·9 for the mobility of the chloride ion. These results imply a Grotthus hopping mechanism, with a favourable rate for the chloride ion transfer reaction:

$$SbCl_3 + SbCl_4^- \rightarrow \overset{.}{S}bCl_4^- + SbCl_3$$

Table 5-4　Limiting conductivities in SbCl$_3$

Salt	Λ_0 (cm^2 ohm^{-1} mol^{-1})	Salt	Λ_0 (cm^2 ohm^{-1} mol^{-1})
KCl	158	KBr	156
RbCl	155		
NH$_4$Cl	152	NH$_4$Br	152
TlCl	149	TlBr	148

5-2-1 Chemical reactions in antimony trichloride

Silver perchlorate dissolves readily in $SbCl_3$ to give a precipitate of silver chloride and a conducting solution. The reaction is probably:

$$AgClO_4 + SbCl_3 \rightarrow AgCl\downarrow + SbCl_2^+ClO_4^-$$

Similarly, $AlCl_3$ and $SbCl_5$ give solutions of high conductivity, e.g.:

$$SbCl_5 + SbCl_3 \rightarrow SbCl_2^+ + SbCl_6^-$$

Conductimetric titrations between such solutions and solutions of tetramethylammonium chloride in the solvent give $1:1$ end-points:

$$Me_4N^+SbCl_4^- + SbCl_2^+ClO_4 \rightarrow Me_4N^+ClO_4^- + 2SbCl_3$$

Solutions of many organic chlorides in $SbCl_3$ are quite good conductors, and it has been shown that these compounds ionize mainly by the reaction:

$$2RCl + SbCl_3 \rightleftharpoons R_2Cl^+ + SbCl_4^-$$

in concentrated solutions.

5-3 Iodine monochloride

Some of the physical properties of iodine monochloride are listed in Table 5-5. Potassium chloride and ammonium chloride are

Table 5-5   Physical properties of iodine monochloride

Melting point (°C)	$27 \cdot 2$ (α), $13 \cdot 9$ (β)
Boiling point (°C)	100
Liquid range (°C)	73
Density (g cm^{-3})	$3 \cdot 24(34°C)$
Specific conductivity (ohm^{-1} cm^{-1})	$4 \cdot 6 \times 10^{-3}(35°C)$
Trouton's constant	$26 \cdot 7$
Enthalpy of vaporization (kcal mol^{-1})	$10 \cdot 0$

moderately soluble in the solvent. So too are RbCl, CsCl, KBr, KI, $AlCl_3$, $AlBr_3$, PCl_5, pyridine, acetamide, and benzamide. All of these compounds yield conducting solutions. LiCl, NaCl, AgCl, and $BaCl_2$ are sparingly soluble. Silicon tetrachloride, titanium tetrachloride and niobium pentachloride dissolve but do not enhance the conductivity. Antimony pentachloride dissolves and increases the conductivity. Thionyl chloride is miscible in all proportions, but simply acts as a diluent and its addition decreases the conductivity of the mixture. However, the mixture is in some ways a much better solvent than either thionyl chloride or iodine monochloride by itself.

Potassium chloride is much more soluble in the mixture than in either of the pure components. This is presumably due to the ability of thionyl chloride to coordinate the cation and iodine monochloride to coordinate the anion.

The importance of self-ionization in the solvent is indicated by the high specific conductivity. Interpretation is complicated by the dissociation into chlorine and iodine. The degree of dissociation is 0·4% at 25°C and 1·1% at 100°C. The self-ionization is probably best represented by:

$$3ICl \rightleftharpoons I_2Cl^+ + ICl_2^-$$

The existence of ICl_2^- in $PCl_4^+ICl_2^-$ and in $KICl_2$ and $RbICl_2$ is well established by X-ray studies. The phase diagrams of the systems $AlCl_3-ICl$ and $SbCl_5-ICl$ show the existence of compounds $AlCl_3, 2ICl$ and $SbCl_5, 2ICl$, which may be formulated as $I_2Cl^+AlCl_4^-$ and $I_2Cl^+SbCl_6^-$. Limiting conductivities, Λ_0, at 35°C of 32 ohm^{-1} cm^2 mol^{-1} for KCl and 26 ohm^{-1} cm^2 mol^{-1} for NH_4Cl are reported. Conductimetric titrations of RbCl against $SbCl_5$ and KCl against $NbCl_5$ show a 1:1 break, and conductimetric titrations of NH_4Cl against $SnCl_4$ show a base:acid break of 2:1.

5-4 Bromine trifluoride

Some of the more important physical properties of bromine trifluoride are listed in Table 5-6. Bromine trifluoride fluorinates virtually

Table 5-6 Physical properties of bromine trifluoride

Melting point (°C)	9
Boiling point (°C)	126
Liquid range (°C)	117
Viscosity (centipoise)	2·22(25°C)
Density (g cm^{-3})	2·8 (25°C)
Specific conductivity (ohm^{-1} cm^{-1})	8·0 × 10^{-3} (25°C)
Trouton's constant	25·6
Enthalpy of vaporization (kcal mol^{-1})	10·2

everything which dissolves in it, so a discussion of solubilities is restricted to soluble inorganic fluorides. The alkali metal fluorides, silver fluoride and barium fluoride, are readily soluble. The fluorides AuF_3, BF_3, TiF_4, SiF_4, GeF_4, VF_4, NbF_5, TaF_5, PF_5, AsF_5, SbF_5, PtF_4, and RuF_5 are also readily soluble. All the above are conductors in BrF_3. Any of the alkali metal or silver or barium fluorides reacts with the Lewis fluorides listed to give a complex halide.

A number of adducts are formed both by the alkali metal fluorides and by Lewis acid fluorides. Thus the alkali metal fluorides form the adducts MF,BrF_3, which can be formulated as $M^+BrF_4^-$. Stannic fluoride forms the adduct $2BrF_3,SnF_4$ and antimony pentafluoride the adduct BrF_3,SbF_5, which may be formulated respectively as $(BrF_2^+)_2SnF_6^{2-}$ and $BrF_2^+SbF_6^-$.

5-4-1 Chemical reactions in bromine trifluoride

Apart from the neutralization reactions already discussed a very large number of complex fluoro-compounds can be prepared in the solvent. Auric fluoride was prepared for the first time by the reaction of metallic gold with BrF_3:

$$Au + BrF_3 \rightarrow BrF_2^+AuF_4^- \rightarrow AuF_3$$

When a mixture of silver and gold is used the compound $AgAuF_4$ is formed.

A mixture of ruthenium metal and potassium chloride is converted into potassium hexafluororuthenate:

$$Ru + KCl \xrightarrow{\text{BrF}_3} KRuF_6$$

Nitrosonium compounds may be produced from nitrosyl chloride and Lewis acid fluorides:

$$NOCl + SnF_4 \xrightarrow{\text{BrF}_3} (NO)_2SnF_6$$

Problems

5-1 The following compounds have been isolated from arsenic trichloride solutions: $Me_4NCl,AsCl_3$; $TeCl_4,2AsCl_3$; $TeCl_4,SbCl_5$; $Me_4NCl,TeCl_4,AsCl_3$; $PCl_5,2TeCl_4,3AsCl_3$; $2TeCl_4,SbCl_5,AsCl_3$. Suggest formulations for them and indicate how you would attempt to verify your formulations.

5-2 What experiments would you carry out to determine whether chloride ion has an anomalous mobility in nitrosyl chloride?

5-3 No one has yet isolated a solid containing the $POCl_2^+$ ion or increased the concentration of $POCl_2^+$ in liquid $POCl_3$. Can you suggest any ways of attempting to do either of these?

Bibliography

1. PAYNE, D. S. Halides and oxyhalides as solvents. Chapter 8 in *Non-aqueous solvent systems*, edited by T. C. WADDINGTON. Academic Press, London and New York, 1965.
2. SHARPE, A. G. The halogens and interhalogens as solvents. Chapter 7 in *Non-aqueous solvent systems*, edited by T. C. WADDINGTON. Academic Press, London and New York, 1965.
3. KOLDITZ, L. Halides of arsenic and antimony, in *Halogen chemistry*, *Vol. 2*, edited by V. GUTMANN. Academic Press, London and New York, 1967.

Fused salts

The chemistry of solutions in fused salts, their equilibria and reactions is of very great technological importance. It is worth recalling that the glass apparatus in which we study the non-aqueous solvents described in Chapters 1–5 is itself a super-cooled complex non-aqueous solution. Most of the industrial metallurgical processes for the extraction of metals involve the use of high temperature melts. It is true that carrying out preparations in the laboratory and obtaining pure products, other than metals, is particularly difficult with fused salts unless the desired reaction product is volatile, but it has been realized recently that in many cases the production of volatile products from molten salt systems is particularly easy and often extremely convenient.

It is not proposed to describe the experimental techniques for obtaining and holding such solutions at constant temperature in this chapter, but some idea of the wide temperature ranges available is given by Table 6-1. Clearly from this table it can be seen that systems are available from just above the boiling point of water to over 2,000°C.

At this point it should be stressed that no completely adequate theory of the molten state is available even for as simple a system as liquid potassium chloride. However, it is possible to discuss the thermodynamics of molten salts and their solutions from a phenomenological viewpoint and gain some information about the structure of molten salts and the entities present in them. Most salts show a sharp increase in conductivity in melting; this, together with the applicability of Faraday's laws of electrolysis and the large temperature range of stability of the liquids, demonstrates the presence of strongly interacting entities, which can only be ions, in molten salts. Although most melts are essentially ionic, there are varying degrees of ionic association shown by different melts. An extreme example of this is mercuric chloride which has a relatively low equivalent conductance and a liquid range of only 26°C, indicating that the melt consists mainly of uncharged molecules.

X-ray and neutron diffraction studies of molten salts enable us to obtain radial distribution curves for the liquids and, from these, coordination numbers and average interionic distances may be found. On melting, in the case of the alkali halides, the number of nearest unlike neighbours decreases from six to an average value of just over four. The average interionic distance of unlike neighbours also decreases slightly, by about 0·15 Å. The radial distribution peaks for second nearest neighbours (like ion interactions) are much

Table 6-1   Melting points (m.p.), boiling points (b.p.), and liquid ranges (l.r.) of some fused salt systems (in °C)

Salt	m.p.	b.p.	l.r.	Salt	m.p.	b.p.	l.r.
LiF	845	1680	835	Li$_2$CO$_3$	726	decomp.	
NaF	995	1704	709	Na$_2$CO$_3$	858	decomp.	
KF	857	1502	645	K$_2$CO$_3$	898		
LiCl	614	1382	768	Li$_2$S	900–975		
NaCl	801	1465	664	Na$_2$S	1180		
KCl	772	1407	635	K$_2$S	840		
LiBr	550	1310	760	Me$_4$NBr	230		
NaBr	750	1392	642	BzMe$_3$NCl	243		
KBr	735	1383	648	BzMe$_3$NBr	235		
LiI	449	1171	722	BzMe$_3$NI	179		
NaI	662	1304	642	(Bu)$_4$NI	144		
KI	685	1330	645	Me$_3$NHCl	271		
LiNO$_3$	254			Et$_3$NHCl	253		
NaNO$_3$	310	(decomp.		Me$_2$NH$_2$Cl	170		
		380)		Et$_2$NH$_2$Cl	223		
KNO$_3$	337			EtMeNH$_2$Cl	126		
KNO$_2$	440			MeNH$_3$Cl	227		
NaOH	320	1390	1070	EtNH$_3$Cl	109		
KOH	400	1327	927	EtNH$_3$Br	159		
Li$_2$SO$_4$	859			EtNH$_3$I	188		
Na$_2$SO$_4$	890			PhNH$_3$Cl	198	245	47
K$_2$SO$_4$	1069	1689	620				

broader than for first neighbours; the numbers appear to have fallen from 12 in the solids to about ten and the distances increased but only slightly.

The volume increase on melting of the alkali halides is fairly considerable (25% for NaCl, 19% for NaI, 17% for KBr, and 16% for KI), and both this and the compressibility of the melts have been explained as being due to the formation of 'holes' in the melt. Such holes may also provide a mechanism for ionic transport through the melt.

What has been said so far applies to the alkali metal halides and many other simple one-component molten salt systems. However, when we come to consider salts with doubly and triply charged cations we have to consider associative equilibria to ion pairs in the melt. Thus:

$$M^{2+} + 2X^- = MX^+ + X^-$$

and a further associative equilibrium is possible:

$$MX^+ + X^- = MX_2$$

With some materials, such as for example $CdCl_2$, further associative equilibria to produce discrete ions such as $CdCl_3^-$ and $CdCl_4^{2-}$ may be possible.

6-1 Methods for the study of molten salt solutions
6-1-1 Cryoscopic methods

If we assume that in a *dilute* solution of a salt in a molten salt the solvent (component in excess) obeys Raoult's Law and the solute Henry's Law, one can apply the Van't Hoff relation:

$$\Delta T = \frac{RT_0^2}{\Delta H_f} \cdot \nu N_{solute}$$

where ν is the number of particles produced per formula unit of solute, N_{solute} is the mole fraction of the solute, ΔH_f is the enthalpy of the solvent, T_0 is the melting point of the pure solvent, and ΔT is the observed freezing point depression. This would then be valid for small values of N_{solute} and for values of ΔT small relative to T_0. The freezing point lowering of $NaNO_3$ by $NaCl$ obeys this equation to about 7 moles % of $NaCl$ for $\nu = 1$. ν must be taken as the number of *independent* particles per formula unit of solute which *differ* from those already present. For example, the solute KCl in the solvent $AgNO_3$ leads to a value of $\nu = 2$, but KNO_3 or Ag_2SO_4 in $AgNO_3$ leads to a value of $\nu = 1$.

Some values of ν for various solutes and solvents are given in Table 6-2, together with their interpretations.

Table 6-2 Numbers of particles produced in various molten salt solutions

Solvent	Solute	ν	Interpretation
$NaNO_3$	Na_2CO_3	1	$2Na^+ + CO_3^{2-}$
$NaNO_3$	$CsCl$	2	$Cs^+ + Cl^-$
$NaNO_3$	Na_2WO_4	1	$2Na^+ + WO_4^{2-}$
$NaNO_3$	$Pb(NO_3)_2$	1	$Pb^{2+} + 2NO_3^-$
$NaNO_3$	$CaCl_2$	3	$Ca^{2+} + 2Cl^-$
$NaNO_3$	$BaCl_2$	3	$Ba^{2+} + 2Cl^-$
$NaNO_3$	$LaCl_3$	4	$La^{3+} + 3Cl^-$

It is worth pointing out that in many systems the limiting law will give no information about complex formation. Thus, if in $NaNO_3$ the reaction of dissolved $Pb(NO_3)_2$ was:

$$2NaNO_3 + Pb(NO_3)_2 \rightarrow 2Na^+ + Pb(NO_3)_4^{2-}$$

one would still expect to find a value of $\nu = 1$. In these cases we cannot use the limiting law and have to investigate the slope of the liquidus line with concentration. However, there are a number of systems where the limiting law can be applied. For example, in dilute solutions of Na_3AlF_6 in Na_2SO_4 a value of 3 is found for ν, corresponding to:

$$Na_3AlF_6(s) = 3Na^+ + AlF_4^- + 2F^-$$

Addition of Na_2TiF_6 to a LiCl–KCl eutectic mixture gives a freezing point depression corresponding to $\nu = 5$, whereas addition of K_2TiF_6 yields a freezing point depression corresponding to $\nu = 3$. These values corresponding to the ionizations:

$$Na_2TiF_6 = 2Na^+ + TiF_4 \text{ (solvated)} + 2F^-$$

$$K_2TiF_6 = 2K^+ + TiF_4 \text{ (solvated)} + 2F^-$$

Presumably species such as $TiF_4Cl_2^{2-}$ and TiF_4Cl^- are formed.

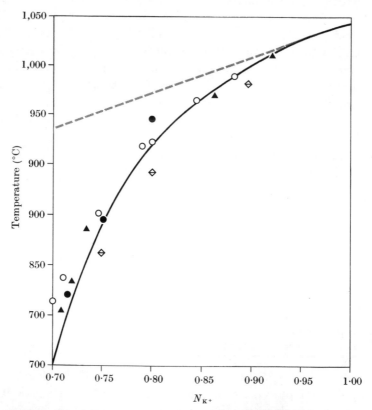

Fig. 6-1   The depression of the freezing point of KCl by the addition of some dichlorides: ⬦, $MnCl_2$; ○, $FeCl_2$; ●, $ZnCl_2$; ▲, $MgCl_2$.

However, on adding K_2TiF_6 and K_2ZrF_6 to KNO_3 values of $\nu = 1$ were found, corresponding to the ionization:

$$K_2MF_6 = 2K^+ + MF_6^{2-}$$

In systems where the limiting law cannot be applied information may sometimes be obtained by treating the system as either an ideal mixture of the two salts or as an ideal mixture of the solvent salt and a complex salt and investigating the variation of freezing point with composition on these assumptions. Fig. 6-1 shows the results of such a study with solutions of $MnCl_2$, $FeCl_2$, $ZnCl_2$, and $MgCl_2$ in KCl. The broken line represents the liquidus calculated on the assumption that the KCl forms an ideal mixture with the dihalides, the continuous line the liquidus calculated on the assumption that KCl forms an ideal mixture with K_2MCl_4.

The results show fairly unambiguously that the complex ions MCl_4^{2-} are formed in KCl solution with the four dihalides. Similar results are obtained with solutions of MnF_2, FeF_2, CoF_2, NiF_2, ZnF_2, MgF_2, and BeF_2 in molten NaF.

6-1-2 Phase diagrams

These have to be interpreted with caution as they do not necessarily give information about the species present in solution. The phase diagrams of many simple systems show no compound formation but simply either a continuous solid solution or eutectic formation. Thus the KF–KCl phase diagram shows a simple eutectic and the KCl–RbCl phase diagram solid solution formation. A list of the behaviour found in some systems is given in Table 6-3. Often compound formation may be produced in the phase diagram of $MX-M'X_2$ systems by

Table 6-3   The behaviour of some molten salt mixtures

Phases	Behaviour	Compounds formed
KCl,RbCl	Solid solution	
LiBr,NaBr	Solid solution	
LiF,NaF	Eutectic formation	
LiF,CsF	Compound formation (incongruent melting point)	$LiCsF_2$
NaF,CsF	Eutectic formation	
LiCl,CsCl	Compound formation	$CsLiCl_2, Cs_2LiCl_3$
KCl,CsCl	Compound formation (incongruent melting point)	K_2CsCl_3
NaCl,MgCl_2	Compound formation (incongruent melting point)	$NaMgCl_3, Na_2MgCl_4$
LiF,BeF_2	Compound formation	Li_2BeF_4
NaF,Na_2SO_4	Compound formation	Na_3SO_4F

increasing the size of the M$^+$ ion. Thus with NaCl,MgCl$_2$ only compounds (NaMgCl$_3$ and Na$_2$MgCl$_4$) with incongruent melting points are produced, whereas in the KCl,MgCl$_2$ system the compounds KMgCl$_3$ and K$_2$MgCl$_4$ have congruent melting points (Fig. 6-2).

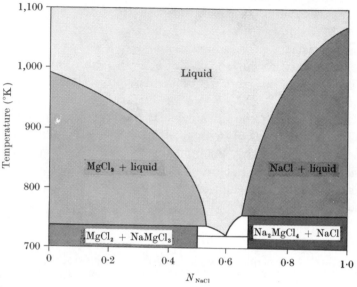

Fig. 6-2   The NaCl–MgCl$_2$ phase diagram.

6-1-3   Spectroscopic measurements

These can be divided conveniently into two types: the investigation of the vibrational spectra and the investigation of the electronic spectra of molten salt solutions. Relatively little work has been done on the vibrational spectra of melts, but what evidence has been accumulated strongly suggests that complex ions can be produced in molten salt systems. The Raman spectra of molten ZnCl$_2$, ZnBr$_2$, CdCl$_2$, HgCl$_2$, and HgBr$_2$ indicate that the dominant species in the liquid are the same as in the crystal. Addition of KCl to molten ZnCl$_2$ produces two new vibrational frequencies, and at 50 moles% KCl the original spectrum of zinc chloride has disappeared. It seems likely that ZnCl$_3^-$ and ZnCl$_4^{2-}$ ions are produced. Similar behaviour is found with molten CdCl$_2$ on addition of KCl. More detailed studies have been made of the HgCl$_2$–KCl molten system. The change in vibrational spectrum with composition has been studied and two species identified, HgCl$_3^-$ and HgCl$_4^{2-}$. The relative intensities of the spectra of the two species have been studied; HgCl$_3^-$ is at a maximum at about 50 moles% KCl and HgCl$_4^{2-}$ at about 66 moles% KCl.

More work has been carried out on the electronic spectra of molten salt systems, particularly on the electronic spectra of transition metal ions in such systems. Here it is often possible to identify the coordination round the transition metal ion. Some results for chloride melts are summarized in Table 6-4. In some of the cases noted in this

Table 6-4   Coordination of transition metal ions in molten chlorides and complex chlorides

Electronic configuration	Species	Solvent	Temperature (°C)	Configuration
d^1	$TiCl_4^-$	$CsGaCl_4$	700	Distorted tetrahedral
	$TiCl_6^{3-}$	LiCl–KCl	400	Distorted octahedral
d^2	VCl_4^-	$CsAlCl_4$	800	Distorted tetrahedral
	VCl_6^{3-}	LiCl–KCl	400	Octahedral
d^3	VCl_4^{2-}	Cs_3ZnCl_4	900	Distorted tetrahedral
	VCl_6^{4-}	LiCl–KCl	400	Octahedral
	$CrCl_6^{3-}$	LiCl–KCl	400–1000	Octahedral
d^4	$CrCl_4^{2-}$	LiCl–KCl	400–1000	Tetrahedral
d^5	$MnCl_4^{2-}$	LiCl–KCl	400–1000	Tetrahedral
d^6	$FeCl_4^{2-}$	LiCl–KCl	400	Tetrahedral
d^7	$CoCl_4^{2-}$	LiCl–KCl	400–1000	Tetrahedral
d^8	$NiCl_4^{2-}$	LiCl–KCl	700–1000	Distorted tetrahedral
d^9	$CuCl_4^{2-}$	LiCl–KCl	400–1000	Distorted tetrahedral

table it seems clear that one can observe, by varying the temperature of the melt, an octahedral–tetrahedral equilibrium. This has been reported to be the case with V^{3+} in a LiCl–KCl eutectic melt. At 400°C the species is predominantly VCl_6^{3-} but at 1,000°C there is a 20% concentration of VCl_4^-. If a fluoride eutectic (LiF–NaF–KF) at 500°C is employed instead of a chloride melt then in the cases of Co^{2+} and Ni^{2+} octahedral coordination is found; this is due to the smaller ionic size of the fluoride ion.

6-1-4   Electrical conductivity and transport properties

A distinction between ionic and molecular melts can be made on the basis of their conductivity. Most molten chlorides have specific conductivities higher than 10^{-1} ohm^{-1} cm^{-1} or lower than 10^{-4} ohm^{-1} cm^{-1}. All the alkali metal halides have specific conductivities in excess of unity.

In mixtures of molten salts, however, it is difficult to obtain more than qualitative data from conductivity studies. If complex ions are formed upon mixing two ionic liquids, then the reduced mobility of the complex ion might be expected to reduce the conductivity below that of either component. In KCl–CdCl$_2$ melts, the decrease in conductivity has been explained in terms of the removal of chloride ions to form $CdCl_4^{2-}$ and $CdCl_6^{4-}$ ions. However, in some systems where the cations are very different in size complex ions may not be formed, but a conductivity minimum may occur; this is found in the LiCl–KCl system.

6-2 Metals in molten salts

So far we have simply considered salts dissolved in molten salts. However, in many cases molten salts are also good solvents for metals and it is worth considering these systems in some detail.

Typical phase diagrams for metal–metal halide systems are shown by the potassium metal–potassium halide systems (Fig. 6-3).

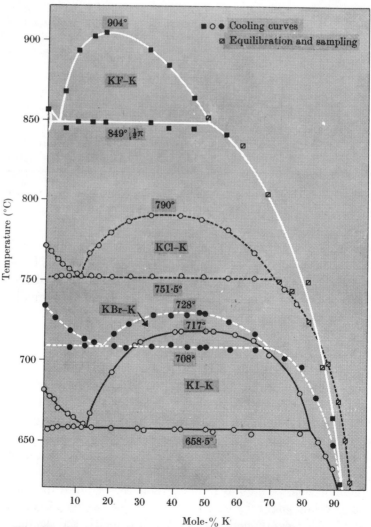

Fig. 6-3 The phase diagrams of the potassium metal–potassium halide systems.

As far as is known there is always a depression of the melting point of the salt by added metal, which terminates at a eutectic point, and beyond that the solubility of metal in the molten salt usually increases with increasing temperature. There is usually a consolute temperature for the two liquid systems. An important feature is the absence of any intermediate solid phase. Another is the very low solubility of the metal halides in the molten metals. The solutions of metal in metal halide are deeply coloured, but little quantitative work has been done on their optical properties. The electrical conductivities of solutions of the alkali metals in their salts are very high and there is a considerable electronic contribution to this conductivity. The variation in equivalent conductivity with concentration are shown for some systems in Fig. 6-4.

Some data on the limiting molar conductivities of sodium and potassium in their halides is given in Table 6-5. It is interesting to

Table 6-5   Limiting molar conductivities, Λ_0, of Na and K in their molten halides at $900°C$ (ohm^{-1} cm^{-2} mol^{-1})

	F	Cl	Br	I
Na	—	6,000	12,000	16,000
K	800	2,800	6,000	8,100

note that the values *decrease* on going from sodium to potassium, but *increase* rapidly from fluoride through to iodide.

Freezing point depression measurements on the solutions of alkali metals in alkali halides at low metal concentrations obey the law:

$$\Delta T = \frac{RT_f^2}{\Delta H_f} \cdot \nu N_{solute}$$

with $\nu = 1$. However, this does not enable one to distinguish between dissolution to neutral atoms ($M°$) or ions and free electrons ($M^+ + e^-$). Conductivity effects favour the latter.

The phase diagrams for the alkaline earth metal–metal halide systems are very similar to those for the alkali metals. The conductivities of the solutions are also high. However, the evidence for the number of particles present per atom of alkaline earth metal dissolved is contradictory. This is for two reasons. One is the experimental inaccuracy of the data, and the second the lack of information about the degree to which the alkaline earth metals form solid solutions in their halides. If solid solutions of appreciable concentration are formed then the simple freezing point depression equation given above cannot be applied. A value of $\nu = 1$ could

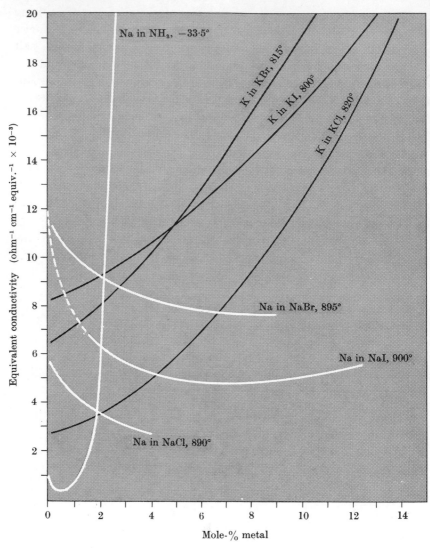

Fig. 6-4 Equivalent conductivities of alkali metal dissolved in their molten halides. (The data for sodium in liquid ammonia are added for comparison.)

be due either to the alkaline earth metal dissolving to give $M°$, or to the formation of M_2^{2+} in solution by the reaction:

$$M + M^{2+} = M_2^{2+}$$

A value of $\nu = 2$ could correspond to:

$$M = M^+ + e^-$$

or

$$M = M^{2+} + 2e^-$$

The increase in conductivity would seem to favour one of these last two equations.

The lanthanide metals are appreciably soluble in the lanthanide trihalide melts and the phase diagrams for these systems show in many cases evidence of compound formation, usually of the dihalide or of a material of intermediate composition between MI_3 and MI_2. The freezing point depressions produced on the addition of Ce to $CeCl_3$, La to $LaCl_3$, Pr to $PrCl_3$, and Nd to $NdCl_3$ indicate that v, the number of particles produced per dissolved atom, is approximately 3. This suggests that either:

$$M + 2M^{3+} = 3M^{2+}$$

or

$$M = M^{3+} + 3e^-$$

Indeed there may very well be an equilibrium occurring:

$$M^{2+} = M^{3+} + e^-$$

The specific conductivities of the metal–metal trihalide solutions support this (Fig. 6-5).

Clearly in the case of neodymium the equilibrium is well over to the left and the system can be regarded as $NdCl_2$ dissolved in $NdCl_3$.

6-3   Systems containing polymerized anions

Such complex anions are formed by salts of Lewis oxy-acids such as SiO_2, B_2O_3, and P_2O_5. The complex anions in such systems are made up of the groups SiO_4, BO_3, and PO_4, which are complexed by the sharing of oxygen atoms. If we adopt the Lux–Flood acid–base definition for such systems we can describe acid–base reactions in such systems as:

$$-\overset{|}{\underset{|}{Si}}-O-\overset{|}{\underset{|}{Si}}- + O^{2-} = -\overset{|}{\underset{|}{Si}}-O^- + {}^-O-\overset{|}{\underset{|}{Si}}-$$

$$\overset{\backslash}{\underset{/}{B}}-O-\overset{/}{\underset{\backslash}{B}} + O^{2-} = \overset{\backslash}{\underset{/}{B}}-O^- + {}^-O-\overset{/}{\underset{\backslash}{B}}$$

and

$$-\overset{|}{\underset{|}{P}}-O-\overset{|}{\underset{|}{P}}- + O^{2-} = -\overset{|}{\underset{|}{P}}-O^- + {}^-O-\overset{|}{\underset{|}{P}}-$$

An oxygen bridge is broken, and two non-bridging oxygens are formed.

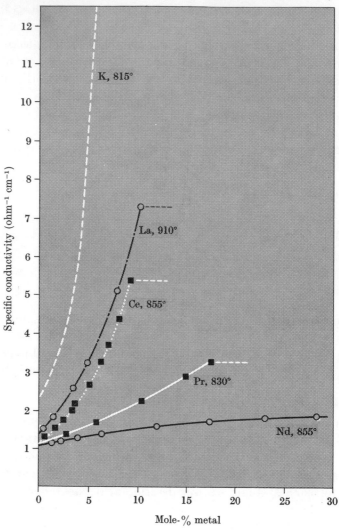

Fig. 6-5 The specific conductivities of some lanthanide metals dissolved in their trichlorides. (The data for potassium in potassium chloride are included for comparison.)

Fused SiO_2 and the silicates are important both from the technology of the glassmaking industry and from the viewpoint of geochemistry. We shall confine our attention to these, but many of the remarks made apply equally well to the systems based on B_2O_3 and P_2O_5.

In the liquid state, silica is completely miscible with the alkali metal oxides. Fig. 6-6 shows the depression of the freezing point of silica by these oxides. The unbroken line is that predicted by Raoult's Law on the basis of $MO_{0.5}$ as the solvent. The systems

Cs_2O-SiO_2 and Rb_2O-SiO_2 follow this line fairly accurately, but with K_2O, Na_2O, and Li_2O there are increasing deviations from ideality. However, they all show that at the limiting concentration the number of solute particles per cation is one. This is presumably because the oxide ions are incorporated into the silicate chains. Thus:

$$2K^+ + O^{2-} + \overset{\textstyle |}{\underset{\textstyle |}{Si}}-O-\overset{\textstyle |}{\underset{\textstyle |}{Si}}- = 2K^+ + \overset{\textstyle |}{\underset{\textstyle |}{Si}}-O^- + {}^-O-\overset{\textstyle |}{\underset{\textstyle |}{Si}}-$$

The increasing deviations from the limiting law line for K_2O, Na_2O, and Li_2O may be due to the increasing formation of clusters of M^+ ions round the non-bridging oxygens. With the alkaline earth oxides, rather different behaviour is found. Ba_2O is completely miscible with SiO_2, but at 2 mole-% shows a freezing point depression only a quarter that of Cs_2O. For the systems SiO_2-MgO, SiO_2-CaO, and $SiO-CaO_2$, separation into two liquid phases occurs. The deviation from ideal behaviour thus seems to increase with increasing field strength of the cation of the base, suggesting that cations with high polarizing powers will be surrounded by a larger number of non-bridging oxygens.

However, when we move to the system $SiO_2-Al_2O_3$ we find that there is no liquid immiscibility. The structures of the solid aluminosilicates show that an aluminium atom can occupy a silicon position.

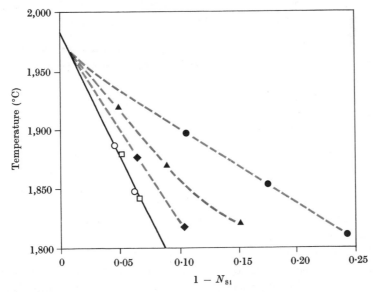

Fig. 6-6 The depression in the freezing point of crystabolite by the alkali metal oxides: ●, Li_2O; ▲, Na_2O; ◆, K_2O; □, Rb_2O; ○, Cs_2O.

If it is assumed that there is completely random occupation of silicon sites by aluminium in the fused SiO_2–Al_2O_3 mixture, the partial molar entropy of mixing is:

$$\Delta \bar{S} = -R \ln \frac{n_{Si}}{n_{Si} + n_{Al}} = -R \ln x_{Si}$$

where n_{Si} and n_{Al} are the numbers of moles of Si and Al and x_{Si} is the mole fraction of Si. Now:

$$\Delta \bar{S} \approx \Delta H_f \left(\frac{1}{T} - \frac{1}{T_f} \right) \approx \frac{\Delta H_f \cdot \Delta T}{T_f^2}$$

so that we can calculate the freezing point depression ΔT. The value calculated is twice the observed value. If instead of a random distribution of silicon and aluminium atoms we assume a random distribution of silicon and *pairs* of aluminium atoms, we obtain:

$$\Delta \bar{S} = -R \ln \frac{n_{Si}}{n_{Si} + \frac{1}{2} n_{Al}} = -R \ln x'_{Si}$$

This gives a freezing point depression in agreement with the observed value. This can perhaps be explained as follows. When two SiO_2 units are replaced by Al_2O_3, two end oxygens must be replaced by a bridged oxygen, e.g.:

$$—O^- + {}^-O— \quad \text{goes to} \quad —O—$$

This is achieved by making two oxygen tetrahedra share an edge, and the lowest cation–cation repulsion energy is obtained when the central atoms of these tetrahedra are Al^{3+} ions.

6-4   Preparative reactions in molten salt systems

The use of fused salts in preparative chemistry and technology is at the moment really confined to two areas. One is the very important one of extractive metallurgy, whereby in a reductive process the metal is obtained from its fused salt (often a natural one) or from a molten solution of its salt by either a chemical or an electrochemical reductive process. The other field is the preparation of volatile compounds by means either of a reaction in the molten state or by a gas–melt reaction. The name of Sundermayer is particularly associated with the development of the latter techniques. The technique that has been employed in the gas–molten salt reaction system is to use a tall reaction cell containing either the binary LiCl–KCl eutectic or the ternary LiCl–NaCl–KCl eutectic as a solvent for a salt. The volatile reactant is then blown through the molten salt in a stream of nitrogen. Some typical reactions are shown in Table 6-6.

Table 6-6 Gas phase–molten salt solution reactions

Volatile reactant	Dissolved salt	Equation	Conditions
Me_3SiCl	CaC_2	$CaC_2 + 2Me_3SiCl \rightarrow$ $Me_3Si \cdot C \vdots C \cdot SiMe_3 + CaCl_2$	CuCl/KCl at 400°C
Me_3SiCl	K_2S	$K_2S + 2Me_3SiCl \rightarrow$ $Me_3Si \cdot S \cdot SiMe_3 + 2KCl$	CuCl/KCl at 400°C
Me_3SiCl	Na_2CN_2	$Na_2CN_2 + 2Me_3SiCl \rightarrow$ $Me_3Si \cdot NCN \cdot SiMe_3 + 2NaCl$	CuCl/KCl at 400°C
Me_3SiCl	NaN_3	$NaN_3 + Me_3SiCl \rightarrow$ $Me_3SiN_3 + NaCl$	CuCl/KCl at 400°C
Me_3SiCl	KCN	$KCN + Me_3SiCl \rightarrow$ $Me_3SiCN + KCl$	CuCl/KCl at 400°C
CH_3Cl	KCN	$KCN + CH_3Cl \rightarrow$ $CH_3 \cdot CN + KCl$	CuCl/KCl at 400°C
F_2CO	KNCO	$KNCO + F_2CO \rightarrow$ $F \cdot CO \cdot NCO + KF$	CuCl/KCl at 400°C
F_2CO	KNCS	$KNCS + F_2CO \rightarrow$ $F \cdot CO \cdot NCS + KF$	NaSCN/KSCN melt

Problems

6-1 Discuss the use of fused salts as solvents for inorganic systems. What physical methods may be used to study the properties of such solutions?

6-2 On dissolving very small amounts of the following pure substances in molten CsCl and measuring the depression of the melting point of the solvent produced by the solute the following values of ν (apparent number of particle per chemical formula unit) were found.

Solute	ν	Solute	ν
RbCl	1	NaBr	2
CsBr	1	$CdCl_2$	1
$BaCl_2$	1	$AlCl_3$	1
Cs_2SO_4	1	Cs	1

Discuss and give equations where possible.

Bibliography

1. BLOOM, H. and J. W. HASTIE. Molten salts as solvents. Chapter 9 in *Non-aqueous solvent systems*, edited by T. C. WADDINGTON. Academic Press, London and New York, 1965.
2. SUNDHEIM, B. R. *Fused salts*. McGraw-Hill, New York, 1964.
3. BLANDER, Milton. *Molten salt chemistry*. Interscience, New York, 1964.
4. LUMSDEN, J. *Thermodynamics of molten salt mixtures*. Academic Press, London and New York, 1966.

Index